ELECTRONIC PROJECTS

CW00348820

Other Titles of Interest

ELECTRONIC PROJECTS
FOR THE GARDEN

by

R. BEBBINGTON

**BERNARD BABANI (publishing) LTD
THE GRAMPIANS
SHEPHERDS BUSH ROAD
LONDON W6 7NF
ENGLAND**

Please Note

Although every care has been taken with the production of this book to ensure that any projects, designs, modifications and/or programs, etc., contained herewith, operate in a correct and safe manner and also that any components specified are normally available in Great Britain, the Publishers and Author do not accept responsibility in any way for the failure, including fault in design, of any project, design, modification or program to work correctly or to cause damage to any other equipment that it may be connected to or used in conjunction with, or in respect of any other damage or injury that may be so caused, nor do the Publishers accept responsibility in any way for the failure to obtain specified components.

Notice is also given that if equipment that is still under warranty is modified in any way or used or connected with home-built equipment then that warranty may be void.

First Published - July 1995

British Library Cataloguing in Publication Data
Bebbington, R.
   Electronic Projects for the Garden
   I. Title
   621.381

   ISBN 0 85934 367 7

Printed and Bound in Great Britain by Cox & Wyman Ltd, Reading

Preface

Browsing through the gardening magazines and the numerous books listed under 'Gardening' in the library, for any signs of electronic gadgets, proved to be a pretty 'fruitless' exercise, if you'll pardon the pun. And there's not a barrow load of gardening ideas to be dug up in the popular electronics press. The fact is that 'electronics' is hardly ever mentioned in the same breath as 'gardening'. The subjects seem to be poles apart, even if names like bulbs, spring clips, spade terminals, banana plugs, branch currents, long-tailed pairs, leaky grids, and a good earth, or ground as the Americans call it, sound vaguely familiar.

Electronics buffs tend to live in a world of their own, and so do the gardening enthusiasts. However, there appears to be a lot of common ground, so here are some useful circuits ideas to help sow the seed to fill it!

You don't need to be an expert in electronics to make any of these gadgets. Some circuits are specially designed for the beginners, and the more adventurous projects can easily be tackled by the average handyman with some basic electrical knowledge. Simple wiring instructions are given and the use of battery power makes for safe circuits.

Roy Bebbington

Contents

Chapter 1

BRANCHING OUT IN ELECTRONICS

Electronica Japonica

Now there's a hybrid to conjure with! You won't find it in any of the gardening books – it's just been coined – because in some respects, branching out in electronics is like turning your hand to gardening. Often, in both fields, you start off with a pack of inert, nondescript objects you can't always identify and follow some simple instructions, hopefully to achieve some end result. You will often have some 'bugs' to iron out before the work you perform on your inanimate objects comes to fruition, but whether it's an amplifier or an anemone you are trying to produce (or reproduce), be assured you can do it without knowing a Latin name like Electronica Japonica, or its atomic structure.

Simple Electronic Systems

Electronic circuits can be useful tools in many down-to-earth situations, and need not be complex to be versatile. The trick is to identify that common-or-garden situation or problem you want to solve and find a suitable electronic circuit to work it out for you.

Although electronic circuits can be very complicated, there are a lot of useful projects that can be constructed using basic systems with just a handful of components. For many simple projects a system consists of three building blocks: an input, a process, and an output stage. For example, take a sneak preview of Figure 2.1 in Chapter 2.

—The input is often a sensor that changes a physical quantity into an electrical signal; e.g. thermistors which detect temperature changes, light-dependent resistors which detect changes in light levels, pressure switches, and microphones that change sound into electrical signals.

—The process can be a single transistor or an integrated circuit, to amplify signals, to oscillate and give a warning tone, or

1

to switch a heavy current device such as a lamp or relay circuit.

—The output device can be chosen to give light, heat, sound or movement; e.g. a lamp or light-emitting diode (LED), a heater, a loudspeaker or an electric motor.

Problem Areas and Solutions

If you are a keen gardener, there must be times when you wish for a bright idea to overcome a certain problem. Perhaps electronics can help!

For instance, watering, or lack of watering, can cause a few headaches. After air and sunlight, water is said to be man's most precious commodity, and judging by that wilting wisteria waiting for water, it could also be said of plants. Despite what people say, you can't be in the garden all the time, and an automatic plant waterer that senses when the soil is too dry, sounds a prime candidate for applied electronics. A handy moisture meter is one of the easier projects to build.

For healthy growth, many plants must be brought on in greenhouses at controlled temperatures. Unheated greenhouses vary widely in temperature, not only seasonally, but over a 24-hour period. Whereas a thermometer will passively indicate this, an active electronic monitoring device can be used to switch on/off soil heaters or close/open greenhouse windows at a preset temperature.

Weather conditions also play an important part for the keen gardener. Frost warnings, heavy rain, high winds need to be taken into account, and a full-blown weather station that monitors all these could be a useful asset.

Security is another area where electronics can be used effectively, not only for intruders and pests, but also for dangerous environmental conditions. Sensing devices can be switch contacts for door and window alarms, light-dependent resistors for smoke, and thermistors for heat alarms.

Finally, ornamental lighting, although not strictly electronic, is a pleasurable attraction well worth including in a garden environment or around a pond. Some form of lighting for paths, steps, garden pools and other potentially hazardous areas also serves to improve general safety during the hours of darkness.

Electricity and Electronics Revisited

At this stage, it may be useful to brush up on your basic electrical and electronic theory to understand how some of these circuits are made to work. Some of the 'nondescript objects' referred to earlier are explained briefly in the charts of Figures 1.1 and 1.2, loosely entitled Electrical and Electronic components.

Some years ago, an elementary book of mine on electronics, aimed at schools, attempted to illustrate the difference between electrical and electronic devices by showing a picture of typical appliances in the home. Broadly speaking, lighting, vacuum cleaners, lawn mowers, etc., were classed as electrical goods, and TVs, radios, tape recorders, etc., as electronic goods. It indicates that devices containing transistors, or valves, are electronic, but the distinction is not clear cut, especially as a flow of *electricity* is in fact *electrons* on the move!

For readers interested in studying the subject further, there are many excellent books in the Bernard Babani (publishing) Ltd list, and popular monthly electronics magazines, that deal with the basic principles in detail.

1. Battery

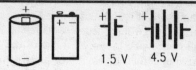

1.5 V   4.5 V

A battery provides electrical energy. It gives out electrons at one terminal and takes them in at the other terminal. The higher the voltage of the battery the more electrons it can force around the circuit.

2. Resistor

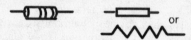

or

Resistors are used to control the flow of electrons (current) around a circuit.
The coloured bands denote the value in ohms (see Chapter 2).

3. Variable Resistor

or

Uses two adjacent connections of a pot.

4. Potential Divider

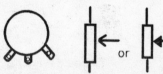

or

Uses all three connections of a potentiometer. The voltage on the slider will vary between the voltages at the two ends.

Fig 1.1   Electrical components

5. Capacitor

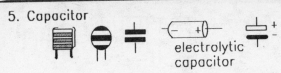

electrolytic
capacitor

Stores electrical charge. Larger values are
electrolytics. Connect the right way round.

6. Diode

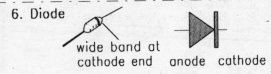

wide band at
cathode end   anode   cathode

Diodes conduct in one direction only,
so can be used to rectify a.c. waveforms.

7. Light−emitting
diode (LED)

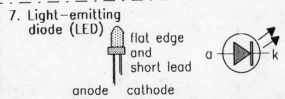

flat edge
and
short lead

anode   cathode

Gives out light when it conducts. Works on 2V;
use limiting resistor if higher voltages in circuit.

8. Transistor

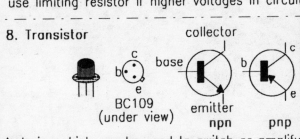

collector

base

BC109
(under view)

emitter
npn

pnp

A device which can be used to switch or amplify.
npn transistors work with the collector positive
with respect to the emitter (reverse for pnps).

Fig 1.2   Electronic components

Chapter 2

A LAYMAN'S APPROACH TO ELECTRONICS

In this age of computers, hi-fi radio and satellite television, nobody can deny that electronics has a tremendous impact on our way of living. Nevertheless, many people know little about the subject of electronics, or even have the desire to know – and why not? We are perfectly free to choose our own interests and these can be so numerous that we have to be selective. Your hobby may be stamp collecting, cricket, football, astronomy, hang-gliding or more likely gardening if you are reading this, which may leave little time to ponder the mysteries of controlling the flow of electrons through a conductor. However, you can regard the field of electronics as a means to an end – a tool that can work for you even if you don't know the finer details!

An electronic system may look complex, but as mentioned in the previous chapter, in reality it can be regarded as a number of basic units each performing a separate function. As mentioned previously, a fundamental system is shown in Figure 2.1 and can be applied to most of the diagrams found in this book. Electronic circuits generally link input devices to output devices to perform a required task.

Often some physical quantity such as sound, light, movement or temperature variation is sensed, transformed into an electrical signal and converted back into a physical quantity to give an output signal. The output signal can perform some task; e.g. operate a pump for instance, or give a monitoring or an alarm signal.

Conductors and Insulators

Electricity can flow easily through metals but not through air or materials like plastics, wood or paper. That's why we use copper wire to conduct electricity around our circuits, and plastics as insulation. Electrons are the tiny negative particles of an atom. All solids contain electrons and particularly in metals these can easily become detached and made to flow from one end of the metal conductor to the other by an 'electrical

7

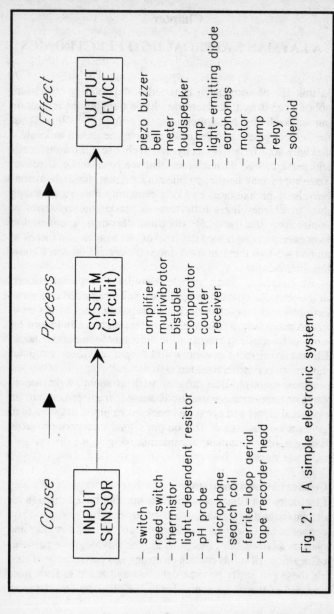

Fig. 2.1 A simple electronic system

Cause → **Process** → **Effect**

INPUT SENSOR

- switch
- reed switch
- thermistor
- light–dependent resistor
- pH probe
- microphone
- search coil
- ferrite–loop aerial
- tape recorder head

SYSTEM (circuit)

- amplifier
- multivibrator
- bistable
- comparator
- counter
- receiver

OUTPUT DEVICE

- piezo buzzer
- bell
- meter
- loudspeaker
- lamp
- light–emitting diode
- earphones
- motor
- pump
- relay
- solenoid

pump'. This 'pump' is a battery, capable of pushing electrons out at one terminal and collecting them in at the other terminal. Remember that the battery is not a source of electrons, like a water pump it just circulates them. The chemicals in the battery provide a reaction to start a current flowing. The strength of this current depends on the pressure difference between the battery terminals. It also depends on how conductive the external circuit is.

Series Circuit

The current in a circuit can be limited by resistance. If we take the simple circuit of Figure 2.2(a) we see that it contains a battery, a resistor and a switch. Resistors are often made of carbon, or nichrome wire, an alloy of nickel and chromium that is not so conductive as the copper conductors. Together, these components form a loop, which we call a series circuit. When the switch is on, the resistor limits the current flowing, warms up, but does nothing useful in this particular circuit. However, if we replace the fixed resistor with a lamp as in Figure 2.2(b), it usefully produces light. To get the most efficient use out of such a circuit, we need to know the relationship between these electrical quantities, voltage, current and resistance. The meters in the circuit measure voltage and current. Note that the voltmeter is connected across the potential difference to be measured and the ammeter is in series with the components. As the same current flows in all parts of the loop, the ammeter can be inserted anywhere in the circuit.

Ohm's Law states that for a given conductor, the ratio of the potential difference across its ends to the current flowing is known as its resistance, measured in ohms.

If we observe the meter readings in the simple circuit of Figure 2.2(a), the meaning of Ohm's Law becomes a little clearer. The potential difference across the resistor is battery voltage, 12V as seen on the voltmeter. The resistor is 60 ohms so the Ohm's Law relationship shows that:

$$I \text{ (current)} = \frac{V \text{ (voltage)}}{R \text{ (resistance)}}$$

therefore,

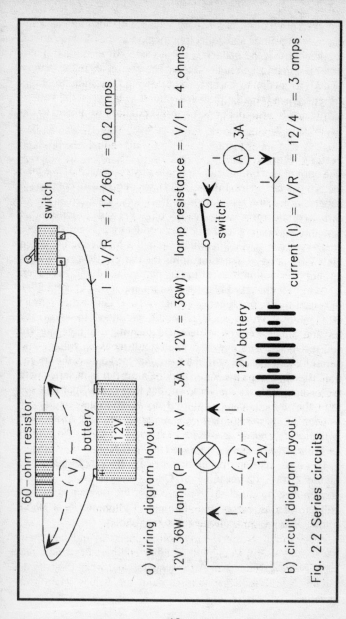

switch

60-ohm resistor

battery
12V

$I = V/R = 12/60 = 0.2\ \text{amps}$

a) wiring diagram layout

12V 36W lamp ($P = I \times V = 3A \times 12V = 36W$); lamp resistance $= V/I = 4\ \text{ohms}$

switch

(A) 3A

12V battery

12V

current (I) $= V/R = 12/4 = 3\ \text{amps}$

b) circuit diagram layout

Fig. 2.2 Series circuits

$$I = \frac{12}{60} = 0.2 \text{ amps}$$

Once you know two quantities in the relationship you can easily work out the third.

But what about the light circuit of Figure 2.2(b)? The lamp is a 12V type with a power rating of 36W. There is also a relationship that states that the power (in watts) equals the product of the current and the voltage ($P = I \times V$). Therefore we can see that the current flowing around the circuit is $P/V = 3$ amps.

The current of 0.2 amps flowing around the circuit of Figure 2.2(a) means the 60 ohm resistor must have a power rating of at least $0.2 \times 12 = 2.4$ watts otherwise it would overheat and possibly burn out.

In Figure 2.2(b) we could of course run two 6V lamps of 18W each in series and the same current of 3A would be drawn from the 12V battery.

Two simple aide memoires in Figure 2.3 will help you calculate these electrical quantities.

Figure 2.4(a) shows two resistors in series across a 12V battery. This network is known as a potential divider since the voltage of the battery divides between these series resistors in proportion to the values of the resistors. Applying Ohm's Law can you find out what the readings would be on the two meters? As shown by the voltmeter, across the smaller resistor R2 there is a smaller potential difference. By Ohm's Law the voltage across the 80-ohm resistor is $V = IR = 0.1 \times 80 = 8V$ and across the 40-ohm resistor is 4V.

Figure 2.4(b) shows a parallel circuit. Notice that in this case it is the current that divides between the two resistors.

Resistors

High resistance values are measured in kilohms (1k = 1,000 ohms) and megohms (1M = 1,000,000 ohms).

Fixed resistors are usually colour-coded to indicate their values. It's useful to know the colour coding so that you can identify the different values for selection and when they are in circuit. You'll soon get familiar with the values when you come to use them.

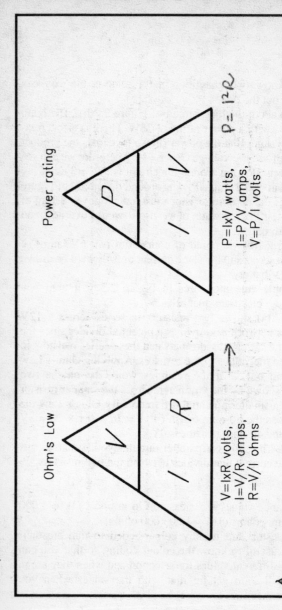

Ohm's Law

$V = I \times R$ volts,
$I = V/R$ amps,
$R = V/I$ ohms

Power rating

$P = I \times V$ watts, $P = I^2 R$
$I = P/V$ amps,
$V = P/I$ volts

To find the quantity you require cover it with your finger – it equals the other two!

Fig. 2.3 Electrical calculation aide memoires

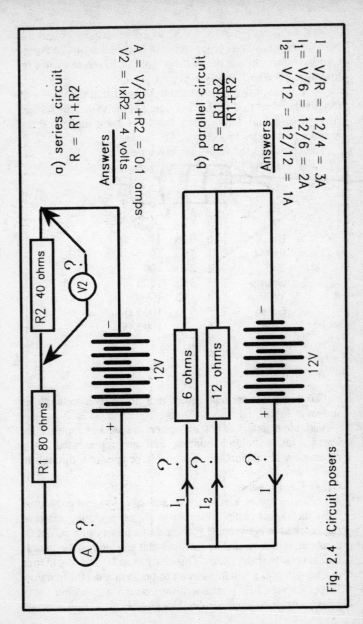

Fig. 2.4 Circuit posers

$I = V/R = 12/4 = 3A$
$I_1 = V/6 = 12/6 = 2A$
$I_2 = V/12 = 12/12 = 1A$

Answers

b) parallel circuit

$R = \dfrac{R1 \times R2}{R1 + R2}$

$A = V/R1 + R2 = 0.1$ amps
$V2 = I \times R2 = 4$ volts

Answers

a) series circuit

$R = R1 + R2$

R2 40 ohms

V2 ?

R1 80 ohms

12V

A ?

6 ohms   12 ohms

12V

I_1 ? I_2 ? I ?

13

Resistors are generally coded by colour bands around the body of the resistor. A group of bands bunched at one end indicate its value while a single band, gold or silver, indicates its tolerance (Gold ±5%; Silver ±10%).

For our purposes, all we need to know is that the colour of the first band represents the first figure of the value, the second band the second figure, and the third band indicates the number of noughts to follow.

The colour-coded values are given below:

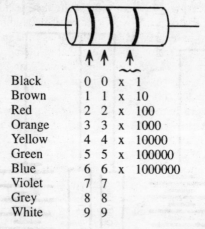

Black	0	0	x	1
Brown	1	1	x	10
Red	2	2	x	100
Orange	3	3	x	1000
Yellow	4	4	x	10000
Green	5	5	x	100000
Blue	6	6	x	1000000
Violet	7	7		
Grey	8	8		
White	9	9		

Fixed resistors are represented in a circuit by a rectangle as shown in Figure 1.1.

Variable resistors or potentiometers are used as controls, for instance as a volume control, and are represented by a rectangle with a short line close to it, or an arrow through it.

Other Components

A *capacitor* stores electricity in a circuit. Modern capacitors have metal foil plates rolled up with an insulating material sandwiched in between. If you connect a battery to a capacitor, a current will flow during the time that an electrostatic charge builds up across the plates. This charge can be stored and then discharged into a suitable circuit to perform a useful function. Direct current (d.c.) cannot flow through a capacitor, so a capacitor can be used for d.c. blocking. However, in a circuit with alternating currents (a.c.), for instance, sound wave signals, a capacitor can control the flow depending on its value, measured in microfarads (µF), or nanofarads (nF), and the frequency of the waveform flowing. Electrolytic capacitors usually provide for the bigger values of capacitance (1µF and over). These are identified by a + sign at one end and must be connected the correct way round in a circuit. The values and maximum working voltages are usually indicated on electrolytic capacitors.

Coils or *inductors* create a magnetic field in a circuit and store energy or control the flow of electricity depending on the value of the coil in henries (H) or millihenries (mH). Coils are used in the metal detector project together with capacitors to make tuned circuits for the oscillators. Circuits can be further tuned by varying the number of turns or by putting a metallic or ferrite core in the coil.

Diodes possess high resistance in one direction and low resistance in the other. Therefore, current flows through a diode or rectifier in one direction only, so, unlike a resistor, it must be connected the right way round. The two lead-out wires are designated anode and cathode; the cathode (+) is indicated by a wide band at one end. A higher voltage at the anode allows a current to flow through to the cathode. Diodes can be used to rectify alternating current to direct current, or to isolate or to group circuits.

Transistors are active semiconductor devices used to switch, amplify and oscillate. The three connections are the emitter, the base and the collector. When measured for resistance, the transistor appears to be two diodes back-to-back. The BC109 used for some of the projects is a general-purpose npn-type silicon transistor.

In amplifier stages, small signal waveforms applied between emitter and base of a transistor produce larger signals at the collector.

Similarly, when transistors are used in oscillator circuits, a small current flowing in the base circuit produces a much larger current in the collector circuit. If this output is fed back into the base in the correct phase it produces an even larger output until the circuit self-oscillates. The frequency of oscillation is determined by tuned circuits.

Integrated Circuits consist of a group of transistors on a small area of silicon crystal interconnected into a circuit. The use of ICs means fewer separate components and connections in a circuit. The dual in-line types used throughout these garden projects include the LM3914 LED display driver, the 555 timer, which incorporated 21 transistors, and the LM386N audio amplifier.

The layout diagrams for ICs show a top view of the pin connections.

Care should be taken when handling ICs as they can be damaged by static electricity. Dual in-line sockets should be used and the ICs fitted last, after circuits are wired.

Soldering

Soldering is a fairly simple operation, but a few golden rules for safety and successful results must be observed:

1. Preferably use a low-voltage soldering iron with a holder. Stray soldering irons lying around on the work bench can be a hazard!
2. Clean the bit by wiping with a wet sponge or fine abrasive paper before starting to solder.
3. Tin the hot iron by melting some solder on to it and wipe it off; the flux in the solder will help to clean it.
4. Make sure that the wires to be soldered are dry and clean.
5. Bring the tip of the hot soldering iron to the joint just long enough to heat the wires.
6. After a few seconds apply the end of the solder to the joint being warmed by the soldering iron. Check that the solder flows freely around both parts of the joint.
7. Remove the solder and iron and allow the joint to cool. A smooth, shiny, well-rounded mound of solder indicates a good joint. On the other hand, a dull blob of solder warns of a 'dry' joint, making poor contact. Dry joints are often caused by tarnished wires or insufficient heat. The remedy is to make sure the wire/copper track is clean and hot enough when the iron is applied for the solder to run freely.
8. Finally, don't use the solder so liberally that it bridges over to other contacts, or tracks, on the stripboard.

Chapter 3

GREENHOUSE DOOR ALARM

Heating a greenhouse can be costly, but not as costly as a sudden drop in temperature that kills off your prize primula pulverulenta. Even if the sun is doing its best to cut down your heating costs, there is no reason to let that precious heat escape because you forgot to shut the greenhouse door behind you. Here's a very simple door alarm that sounds automatically if you inadvertently leave the door open for more than a few seconds. And for those occasions when you are constantly in and out, or the heat gets oppressive, there's an override switch so that you can prop the door open without alarming or alerting the neighbourhood. As this simple device also serves as an intruder alarm it makes sense to locate the override switch out-of-sight of would-be garden gangsters.

Circuit

To give a gentle lead-in, the circuit shown in Figure 3.1 has purposely been made very simple, and for those new to electronics it provides an ideal introduction. As explained under the heading 'Construction', you don't even need to do any soldering if you get the right components.

Basically, the circuit consists of the switching transistor (TR1) controlled by an electrolytic capacitor (C1) charging through a resistor (R1). A miniature 6V solid-state buzzer (WD1) is activated when the transistor switches on after a pre-arranged delay. Normally, switch contacts (S1) operated by the closed door of the greenhouse short-circuit the capacitor. Therefore, in this condition the base of the transistor is connected to zero volts and so it will not conduct. When the greenhouse door is opened, the switch contacts open and the 9-volt positive supply from battery BY1 is fed via resistor R1 to charge capacitor C1. The values of R1 and C1 are chosen so that C1 charges slowly.

If S1 is released (by closing the door) within a few seconds, then the capacitor will not have had time to charge sufficiently to switch on transistor TR1 before it is short-circuited by S1.

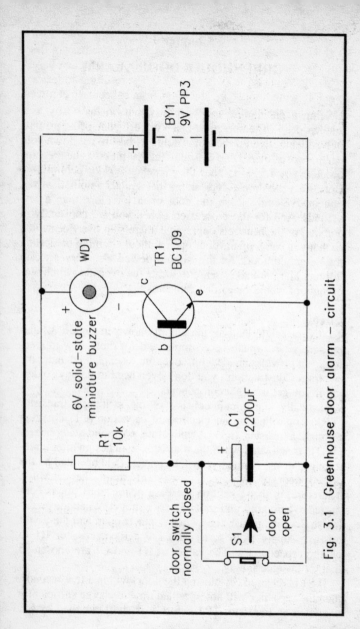

Fig. 3.1 Greenhouse door alarm – circuit

WD1

6V solid–state
miniature buzzer

TR1
BC109

R1
10k

C1
2200μF

BY1
9V PP3

door switch
normally closed

S1

door
open

However, if S1 is not released, i.e. the door is left open, then C1 continues to charge and the voltage level at the base of the transistor increases. At a voltage around 0.7V, sufficient base current flows via R1 to switch on TR1. The resulting collector current flowing through the transistor from collector to emitter activates the electronic buzzer.

Shutting the door closes S1 contacts which discharge C1, so resetting the circuit delay ready for the next time.

The delay of a few seconds allows you to go in and out of the greenhouse briefly without the alarm sounding. If this delay time is too short, then increase the value of either R1 or C1 accordingly.

An override switch can be fitted as suggested in series with the battery, or simply unclip the battery. Another way to disarm the alarm is to fit a retaining strip on the door frame to hold switch S1 in when the door is permanently open.

The quiescent current drawn by this circuit is less than 1mA, so a 9V PP3 battery should last for some considerable time.

Construction

There are only half a dozen components to connect in this project, so to make things easy, the circuit could be mainly constructed on a terminal block using a screwdriver (see Figure 3.2). If you prefer using a terminal block, ensure that you get an electrolytic capacitor with end wires to screw into the block, otherwise you will need to resort to wrap-around connections or soldering. However, soldering is not difficult, as explained in Chapter 2, so a wiring layout on stripboard is included in Figure 3.3 for those who are competent or willing to have a go.

Switch S1 may be a push-to-break, non-locking pushbutton type, or the break connections of a microswitch. Alternatively, a pair of break contacts can be affixed to the door frame. As stated, a simple override device in the form of a retaining strip can be used to hold in the S1 contacts to inhibit the door alarm when you need to leave the door open for a short period.

Components for Greenhouse Door Alarm (Fig. 3.1)

Resistor
R1   10k

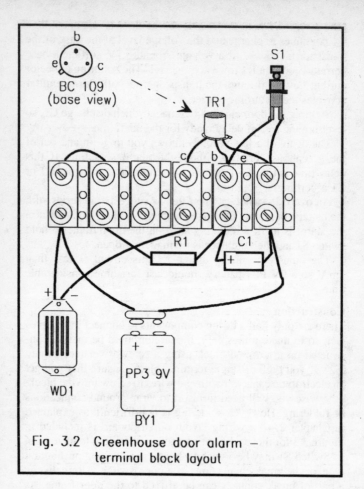

Fig. 3.2 Greenhouse door alarm —
terminal block layout

Capacitor
C1   2200µF 35V elect

Semiconductor
TR1   BC109 or similar

Switches
S1   push-to-break, non-locking (see text)

20

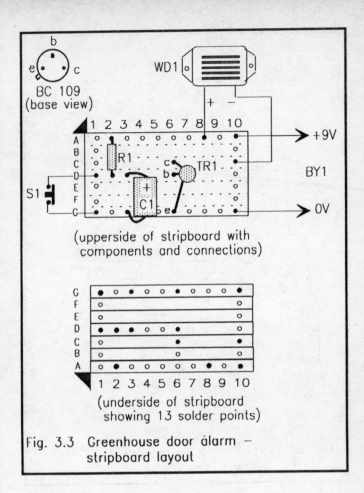

Fig. 3.3 Greenhouse door alarm –
stripboard layout

Battery
BY1   9V PP3 with clip

Miscellaneous
6-way screw-type terminal block, or 0.1-in pitch stripboard (7 strips × 10 holes), multi-strand insulated connecting wire, solder, etc. A small piece of plywood to mount the project.

Chapter 4

AUTOMATIC PLANT WATERER

Plants, like humans, are not happy to go without water for long periods, and it's not always convenient to be on hand to quench their thirst. Gravity feeds and good neighbours may help, but here's an automatic watering circuit that will water your tomatoes when the soil gets too dry during the night. Extra switching can be included to operate the water pump manually when desired, and for plants that need automatic watering day and night.

Basic System Requirements
The circuit uses logic gates to operate a relay, the contacts of which switch on the water pump. Initially, two conditions are stipulated before the system switches on the pump. These are as follows:
  – the pump must be activated when the soil dries out;
  – it must only be during the hours of darkness.
To satisfy these requirements two sensors are used. The dry condition is sensed by the resistance between two probes placed in the soil, and the light, or lack of it, is sensed by a light-dependent resistor suitably located to catch the ambient light.

Circuit
The process logic is performed by a CMOS integrated circuit IC1. This uses two gates of a quad two-input NAND gate as shown in Figure 4.1.

The circuit operates in the following way. Light-dependent resistor PCC1 is connected between input pin 1 of the first gate and the 0V rail. Potentiometer VR1 is adjusted so that during daylight the input to pin 1 is low. The probes embedded in the soil being sampled are connected between input pin 2 and the 0V rail. Potentiometer VR2 is adjusted so that when the soil is moist the input to pin 2 is also low. By design, either, or both, of these conditions will prevent the output relay RLA from operating, because one low input on the first NAND gate will

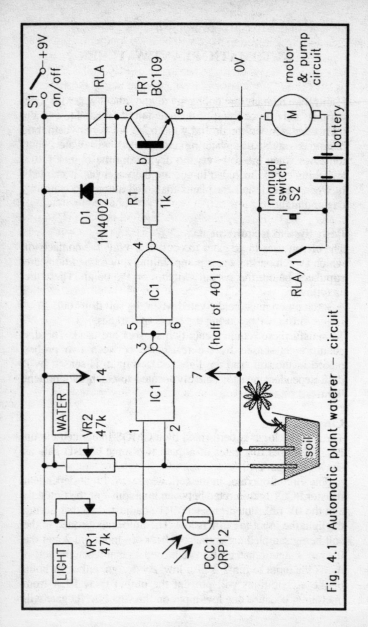

Fig. 4.1 Automatic plant waterer – circuit

24

make its output (pin 3) high. Consequently, because the second gate acts as an inverter, there will be a low output on pin 4 and transistor TR1 will not conduct.

However, if it is dark, the resistance of PCC1 goes high, and as VR1 and PCC1 act as a potential divider across the +9V supply rail, there will now be more voltage on input pin 1 of the first IC1 gate. In addition, if the soil sample dries up, then the resistance between the probes will go high. Likewise, because VR2 and the resistance between the probes also act as a potential divider, there will be more voltage on input 2 of the first IC1 gate. When these two inputs are both at logic 'high', then the output of the first NAND gate (pin 3) goes low. Consequently, this low output, which is connected to input pins 5 and 6 of the inverter results in a high output on pin 4. This logic 'high' provides base current for TR1, which switches on and activates relay RLA in the collector circuit. The catching diode D1 prevents any damage to the transistor due to the reverse voltage spike produced by the relay coil at switch off.

Note that the motor and pump are activated by the relay contact as an independent circuit or by a manual override switch. Low-voltage motors, pumps and watering systems are commercially available from suppliers and garden centres. The prime object of this automatic plant waterer circuit is to supply a pair of contacts that can switch on such equipment when the desired environmental conditions are present. **This circuit is for use ONLY with low voltage motors and pumps.**

Construction
Figure 4.2 shows the component layout on a 0.1-in matrix stripboard. In addition to the component wiring for R1, D1 and TR1, the inputs of the spare gates of IC1 are strapped to the supply lines to avoid instability. Breaks in the copper tracks must be made between the opposite pins of IC1 as shown in the rear layout diagram, Figure 4.3.

Note that the relay contacts of RLA must have adequate current capacity for the pump circuit chosen.

Components for Figure 4.1

Resistor
R1   1k

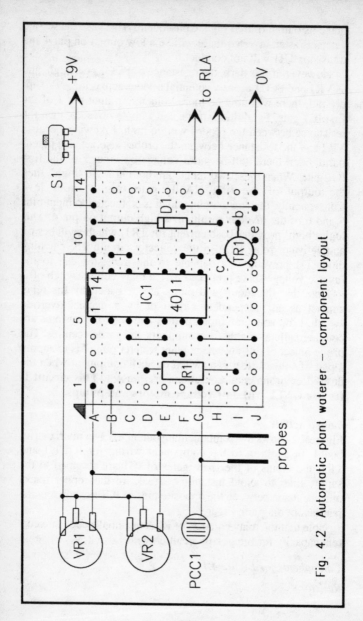

Fig. 4.2 Automatic plant waterer – component layout

26

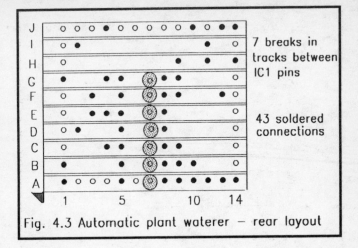

Fig. 4.3 Automatic plant waterer — rear layout

Potentiometers
VR1   47k
VR2   47k

Semiconductors
IC1   4011 quad 2-input NAND gate
TR1   BC109
PCC1   light-dependent resistor ORP12
D1   diode 1N4002

Relay
RLA   6–9V relay with make contact

Switches
S1   S.P.S.T.

Miscellaneous
Stripboard, 9V battery and connector, small project box
suitable for mounting two potentiometers, switches, PCC1
light-dependent resistor, relay and circuit board; thick copper
wire probes, wiring, etc.

Chapter 5

TEMPERATURE MONITORING

Temperamental Temperatures!
Plants that live in glass houses, should not be subjected to violent changes of temperature. No! it's not a horticultural proverb, but there's a lot of truth in it. Much of the success of a greenhouse depends on the proper ventilation and regulation of its heat and moisture. There's nothing more calculated to kill off a greenhouse full of prize plants than a ventilator open when it should be closed and vice versa. Like humans, plants are susceptible to violent temperature changes; they don't like to be scorched by the intense heat of the summer sun, or withered by a chilling breeze.

As most gardeners know, the optimum temperatures for a greenhouse vary with the plants to be grown in it. Suitable candidates for your particular greenhouse temperature ranges can easily be found by reference to catalogues and instruction leaflets. As a rough guide, the mean temperatures of cool, warm and hot houses are given below:

	SUMMER	*WINTER*
COOL GREENHOUSE		
Day	60-65 deg.F (16-18 C)	55-65 deg.F (13-18 C)
Night	55-60 deg.F (13-16 C)	45-50 deg.F (7-10 C)
WARM GREENHOUSE		
Day	65-75 deg.F (18-24 C)	60-70 deg.F (16-21 C)
Night	60-70 deg.F (16-21 C)	55-65 deg.F (13-18 C)
HOT GREENHOUSE		
Day	70-85 deg.F (21-29 C)	65-75 deg.F (18-24 C)
Night	65-75 deg.F (18-24 C)	60-70 deg.F (16-21 C)

Whatever kind of heating is used to control these daily and seasonal temperatures, it is essential that there is some method of monitoring over these ranges. At least, measurement of temperature, if not the temperature control, should be done automatically as it's impossible to be on constant guard duty, day and night, summer and winter. And talking of winter, it might be handy to have a frost alarm warning so that you can cover up your glass frames when the weather starts to get chilly.

The following circuits show how to monitor a chosen set-point, sounding an alarm when it is reached. The basic circuits can easily be re-arranged for high or low set-points, or both if you want to monitor a permissible range of temperature.

Frost Alarm Circuit

A simple frost alarm circuit is shown in Figure 5.1. The increase in resistance of a n.t.c. (negative-temperature coefficient) thermistor as the temperature lowers is used to switch on a transistor and bring on an alarm. The circuit operates as follows.

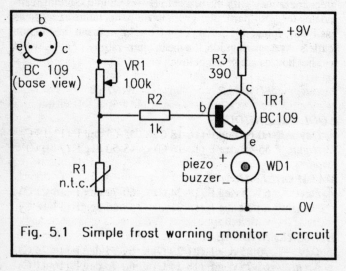

Fig. 5.1   Simple frost warning monitor − circuit

The n.t.c. thermistor R1 and the variable resistor VR1 form a potential divider across the 9V supply and provide base current via R2 to the npn transistor TR1. To calibrate the circuit, immerse the thermistor in iced water, ensuring the leads do not get wet, and adjust the variable resistor VR1 until the piezo buzzer WD1 in the emitter circuit is just activated. Removing the thermistor from the water will increase its temperature and reduce its resistance, causing the alarm to stop. Check that the alarm sounds again when the thermistor is immersed in the iced water.

Other under-temperature limits other than freezing point can be set if desired by adjusting and calibrating VR1. For instance, on a cold winter's night, you may wish to monitor the 45 degrees Fahrenheit set-point as an alarm indication. To calibrate this, immerse the thermistor into some water cooled to 45 deg.F – checked with a thermometer – and adjust VR1 until the piezo buzzer just sounds.

Alternatively, this circuit can be adapted as an over-temperature monitor by reversing the positions of R1 and VR1. Obviously, it will be necessary to re-calibrate VR1 to suit the new set-points.

No great accuracy is claimed for this simple circuit; as the thermistor is an analogue device, the buzzer tends to come on gradually. However, it does give a timely warning that 'everything in the garden is *not* lovely!'.

The frost warning monitor can be wired up in a few minutes on an electrical terminal block, using a small screwdriver. The layout is shown in Figure 5.2, and is self-explanatory. The component list for the circuit is given at the end of this chapter.

Improved Over-Temperature Monitor Circuit

By using a comparator circuit we can get a faster snap-over action when our set-point voltage is exceeded. Figure 5.3 shows the circuit details. Integrated circuit IC1, a 741 op-amp compares the voltages of two inputs, a reference potential and the thermistor potential, and provides an output signal to a transistor, TR1, with a piezo buzzer, WD1, in its emitter circuit.

A reference voltage of 4.5V is applied to the positive input, pin 3 of IC1, by the potential divider R1, R2. Thermistor R3 and variable resistor VR1 provide a potential divider network for the negative input, pin 2 of IC1. The alarm is inactive if VR1 is adjusted so that the voltage on pin 2 is above the reference voltage on pin 3. However, as the thermistor warms up, its resistance decreases, and the potential on pin 2 falls below the

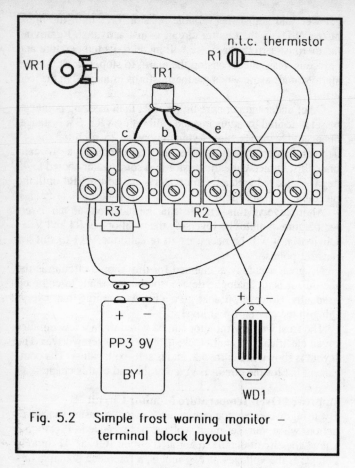

Fig. 5.2   Simple frost warning monitor –
terminal block layout

reference voltage. This potential difference between the two
inputs causes the output voltage on pin 6 to swing positive. The
resistor R4 provides small positive feedback, which gives a
quick snap action when the comparator switches on or off. A
positive on output pin 6 provides base current via R5 to switch
on TR1 and operate buzzer WD1.

    The value of the variable resistor VR1 should be
selected according to the type of thermistor in use. For instance,
for a GL16 bead-type thermistor, increase the value of VR1 to

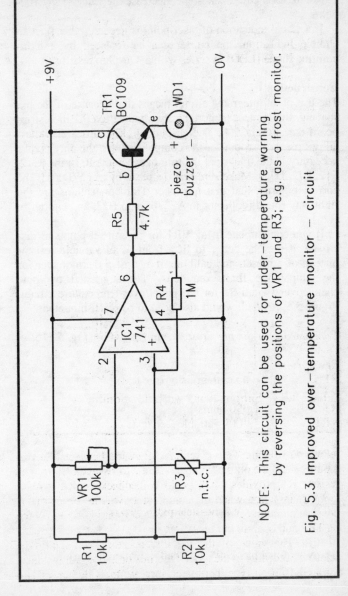

NOTE: This circuit can be used for under-temperature warning by reversing the positions of VR1 and R3; e.g. as a frost monitor.

Fig. 5.3 Improved over-temperature monitor – circuit

33

1M-ohm; for a GL23 bead-type, decrease the value to say 10k-ohms.

If a visual indication of a set-point is needed rather than an audible indication, the buzzer can be replaced by a light-emitting diode (LED) in series with a 470-ohm resistor.

Construction

The use of an integrated circuit means that because of the pin spacing, this project is more easily mounted on 0.1 inch strip-board (see Figure 5.4). The stripboard (12 strips × 23 holes) allows plenty of room for the components and the only breaks necessary in the tracks are the four between the IC1 pins (G12, F12, E12, D12). Make sure that the piezo buzzer WD1 has the correct polarity, and that transistor TR1 connections are the right way round (collector to A22, base to B22, and emitter to H22).

If you contemplate using VR1 for several set-points as discussed, it may be better to fit a front panel variable resistor instead of a preset, and calibrate it against a thermometer for the temperature limits required. The suggested two-pole changeover switch S1 for the under/over-temperature circuit, Figure 5.5, if fitted, would also need to be panel-mounted.

Components for Simple Frost Warning Monitor (Fig. 5.1)

Resistors

R1	n.t.c. thermistor (see text)
R2	1k
R3	390 ohms
VR1	100k variable (see text)

Semiconductor

TR1	BC109

Loudspeaker

WD1	6V solid-state piezo buzzer

Miscellaneous

6-way terminal block, 9V PP3 battery with clip, wiring.

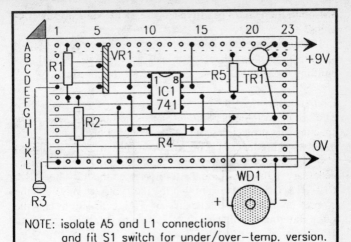

NOTE: isolate A5 and L1 connections
and fit S1 switch for under/over-temp. version.

(topside of stripboard showing components and links)

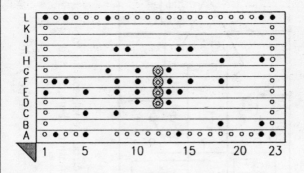

(underside of stripboard showing solder points)

Fig. 5.4 Improved over-temperature monitor
   – stripboard layout

35

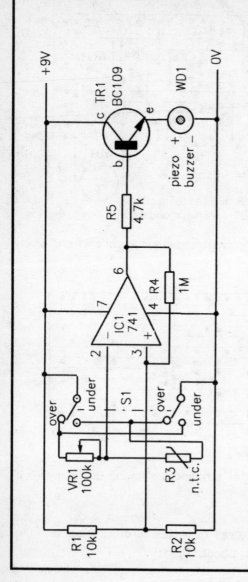

NOTE: This circuit enables the monitor to be switched for under-temperature monitoring at night, and for over-temperature monitoring during the day.

Fig. 5.5 Improved under/over temperature monitor – circuit

36

Components for Improved Over-Temperature (Fig. 5.5)

Resistors
R1, R2   10k (2 off)
R3   n.t.c. thermistor (see text)
R4   1M
R5   4.7k
VR1   100k variable resistor (see text)

Semiconductors
TR1   BC109
IC1   741 op-amp

Loudspeaker
WD1   6V solid-state piezo buzzer

Switch for Under/over-temperature facility
S1   2-pole rotary changeover

Miscellaneous
Stripboard 0.1-inch matrix (12 strips × 23 holes), 8-pin d.i.l.
holder, 9V PP3 battery with clip, insulated wiring.

Chapter 6

RAIN AND FLOOD WARNINGS

The amount of rainfall is easily measured by an open container suitably calibrated in centimetres or inches. However, the keen gardener, or perhaps whoever hangs out the washing, is usually more interested to know when it starts to rain. Fortunately, a sudden downpour can easily be sensed by a simple electronic circuit and a visual or audible warning given in the house or at some other remote location.

Forewarned is forearmed, and in the more disastrous event of flooding, it is better to have prior warning than to wait for that dreaded trickle of water under the door. Here again, a flood level monitoring circuit is not difficult to construct. However, we will first consider the rain monitor.

Rain Monitor
Most of us listen to the weather forecast, observe cloud formations, or sense for rain by sticking our hand out of the window. For monitoring purposes in the garden there is a 'growing' need for an electronic sensor for detecting rain. This monitor circuit depends on the principle that rainwater contains sufficient impurities to conduct electricity. As an improvement on using our hand as a sensor, we can make use of a small wire frame that collects raindrops between the wires and causes a current of electricity to flow to operate an alarm. This sensor frame must of course be exposed to the elements. In other words, it's plain we must ensure that the rain falls mainly on the frame!

Rain Monitor Circuit
The rain monitor circuit of Figure 6.1 uses two transistors in a simple switching circuit using the principle described. The small sensor frame consists of two parallel copper wires spaced a raindrop apart, or a small piece of stripboard as shown. The resistor R1, the sensor wires, and potentiometer VR1 form a potential divider between the +9V and 0V rails.

Under dry conditions the base of the npn transistor TR1 is held low by VR1. However, when the sensor is bridged by

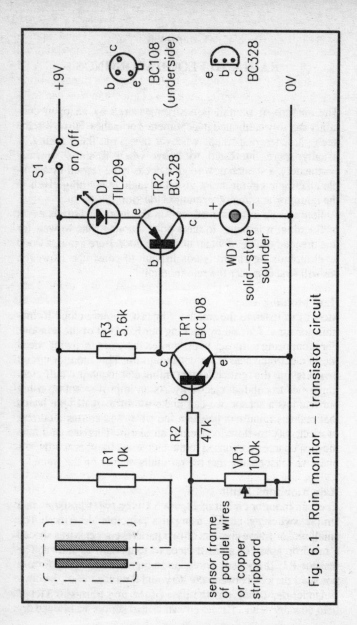

Fig. 6.1 Rain monitor – transistor circuit

40

raindrops it acts as a resistance in series with R1 and a potential is applied to the base of TR1 via R2. This potential will depend on the resistance of the sensor and the value of VR1. Potentiometer VR1 should be adjusted so that a raindrop bridging the sensor just brings TR1 into conduction. You can test it by touching a moist finger on the sensor and adjusting VR1 until the alarm sounds. This causes TR1 collector voltage to fall.

Normally – during dry weather – TR1 will not conduct and so the base of the pnp transistor TR2 is held off by the +9V via R3. However, when TR1 conducts, the base of TR2 falls towards 0V and the transistor conducts, bringing on the light-emitting diode D1 and the solid-state sounder WD1. The circuit will reset itself when the sensor dries off, but can be switched off manually by S1 if the rain is persistent.

Construction

As the rain monitor circuit is straightforward, it's an ideal project for demonstrating a simpler construction method for the beginner than using stripboard. The breadboard layout diagram of Figure 6.2 is almost self-explanatory. It consists of mounting the components on a small block of plywood, using metal-headed drawing pins as anchor points. Soldering to the heads of the drawing pins poses no problems, and there is ample room on the heads if two connections are to be made per pin. If connections are spaced out on the head, the first will not be disturbed when soldering the second unless you linger too long with the soldering iron. Alternatively, you can tap in small brass or copper tacks for anchor points, in which case it is advisable to wrap the leads around before soldering.

For convenience, this breadboard layout closely follows the circuit diagram layout of Figure 6.1. Physical layouts can of course be in any convenient form with the restriction that leads in general, and input leads in particular, should be as short as possible. However, when drawing circuit diagrams, lines are generally squared up for ease of reading, and the positive and negative rails are usually along the top and bottom respectively. Inputs are conventionally positioned on the left of the drawing and outputs are on the right. The wiring on the breadboard can be made with short lengths of tinned copper wire. Take care

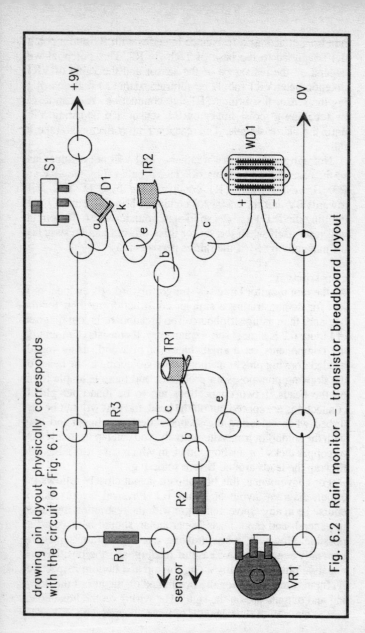

drawing pin layout physically corresponds
with the circuit of Fig. 6.1.

Fig. 6.2 Rain monitor – transistor breadboard layout

42

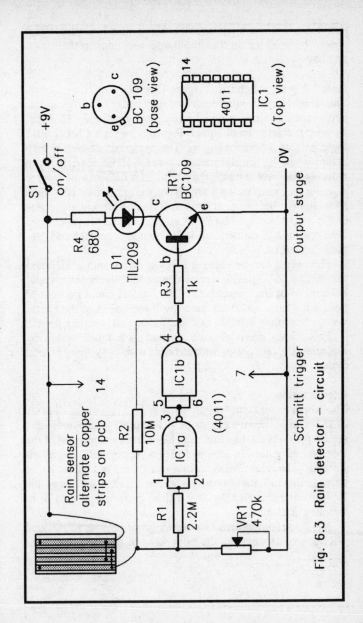

Fig. 6.3 Rain detector – circuit

43

that there are no short-circuits. Multi-strand covered wire should be used for the flexible interconnections to the sensor and battery, etc.

Rain Detector – Schmitt Trigger Circuit

The simple rain monitor described may not easily differentiate between a shower of rain or a misty moisty morning. To sharpen up the voltage input signal, Figure 6.3 uses a CMOS 4011 logic gate as a Schmitt trigger. The hysteresis ensures a snap action when the transfer voltage is reached; i.e. there is a gap between the level at which the circuit goes high and the level at which it returns to its low state. When the rain sensor is bridged by a raindrop the inputs of inverter IC1a go high and give a low at the output pin 3. In turn, via inverter IC1b, this produces a high on pin 4, base current via R3 switches on TR1 and produces an output.

The output can be either a LED in series with a 680 ohm resistor, or a 6V relay. If a relay is used then the contacts could be used to operate equipment. One contact could be used to hold pin 4 high and latch the relay if the object of the circuit was to determine whether rain had fallen over a certain period.

This circuit could also be adapted as a touch switch by replacing the rain sensor with a couple of closely-spaced metal pads.

Construction

The rain detector layout (Figures 6.4 and 6.5) uses a small piece of 0.1-inch stripboard (10 strips × 13 holes) to accommodate the 14-pin 4011 dual-in-line chip. Note that the input pins of the two unused gates are strapped to the supply rails to prevent instability. Normal CMOS precautions should be taken to avoid damage due to static. For instance, use a d.i.l. holder, keep the IC in its original packing until wiring is complete, then fit it, handling it carefully.

The three components external to the stripboard, S1, D1 and VR1 can be mounted on the front panel of a small plastic project box.

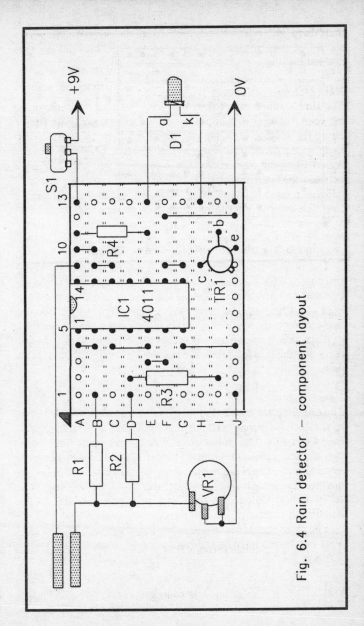

Fig. 6.4 Rain detector – component layout

45

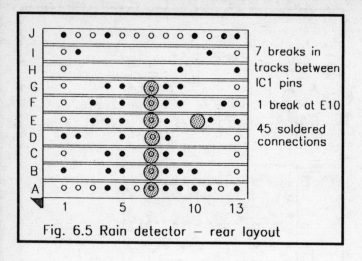

Fig. 6.5 Rain detector — rear layout

Components for Rain Monitor (Fig. 6.1)

Resistors

R1	10k
R2	47k
R3	5.6k

Potentiometers

VR1	100k

Semiconductors

TR1	BC108
TR2	BC328
D1	LED TIL209

Switches

S1	S.P.S.T. (on/off)

Alarm

WD1	9V solid-state sounder

Components for Rain Detector (Fig. 6.3)

Resistors
R1   2.2M
R2   10M
R3   1k
R4   680

Potentiometer
VR1   470k

Semiconductors
IC1   CMOS 4011 quad 2-input NAND-gate
TR1   BC109
D1   LED TIL209

Switches
S1   S.P.S.T. (on/off)

Miscellaneous
Small project box, stripboard (10 strips × 13 holes), 9V battery,
wire, etc.

Chapter 7

ELECTRONIC WATCHDOGS

Security in the garden may well be important to you, particularly if you're a keen gardener, or store valuable equipment in your greenhouse or garden shed. There are several circuits that can be easily constructed to deter vandals or a potential intruder. For example, the rain detector probes in Chapter 6 could be replaced with sensor contacts to serve as a make-to-operate alarm.

Light-sensitive Alarm
Here again, the simple light/dark detector circuit described in Chapter 9, can be used as an intruder alarm in the light-activated mode. If the light-cell sensor is illuminated by an intruder's torch or if a light is switched on, then the relay contacts can switch on an alarm buzzer or indicator light to alert the householder.

Greenhouse Door Alarm
A simple door alarm, primarily intended as a reminder to 'shut that door!', is described in Chapter 3. However, as it is no respector of persons, it can also perform in a security role as an intruder alarm.

Bogus Greenhouse Alarm
Before we look at some more functional security circuits, here's a watchdog circuit that can keep an eye on things for you. It has only one eye, a tri-colour LED, but, as the title implies, it's a watchdog with no teeth! The tri-colour LED flashes slowly from green to red, but does nothing else. It is merely intended to deter a would-be intruder, but as it is such a simple circuit to make up, it could amply repay the effort if it intrigued 'chummy' and made him think twice. Besides, it is so small that, as a bonus, it could rest on the dashboard of your parked car and serve a dual-purpose as a **'bogus auto alarm'**.

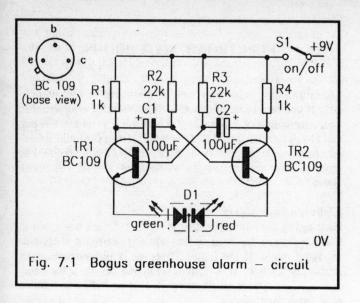

Fig. 7.1 Bogus greenhouse alarm — circuit

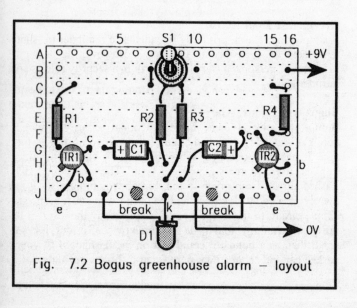

Fig. 7.2 Bogus greenhouse alarm — layout

Circuit

The circuit of Figure 7.1 is an astable multivibrator using two general-purpose npn transistors, type BC109. These transistors (TR1, TR2) are cross-coupled by electrolytic capacitors C1 and C2. As these capacitors charge up, the changing voltages are applied to each transistor so that they switch on and off in turn. The rate at which they flip on and off depends on the time constants of components C1, R2, and C2, R3. The values chosen will give a flip-over between red and green in the emitter LED, D1, about every second or so. To vary the speed, change the values of these components. Reducing the values will mean that D1 will change colour faster; increase the values to slow down the changeover.

Construction

A small piece of stripboard (Figure 7.2) is used for the few components that make up the circuit. Note that two breaks are made in the copper strip side to accommodate D1. The common cathode of D1, the middle leg, is connected to the centre of the 0V strip. The circuit can be housed in a small plastic project box with the LED displayed on the front.

Simple Contact-operated Alarms

Contact-operated alarms need not be over-elaborate to be effective. The important rule is to locate the switch sensors in positions the prowler cannot avoid operating them, and to keep wires, sensors and equipment out of sight and reach. Doors and windows by which burglars can gain access, or inviting mats on which to wipe their muddy feet, can be wired with 'make' or 'break' contacts, strips of foil, or pressure pads. The simplest circuit that springs to mind is an extra remote 'make' contact, or several, wired in parallel with an existing door bell-push.

The main snag with this kind of circuit is that the alarm only indicates a general caller, and unless the 'make' contact is designed to persist, the bell will only sound briefly.

Self-latching 'Make' Alarm

To overcome this problem we can resort to a relay-operated bell or sounder, with an extra relay 'make' contact to latch the

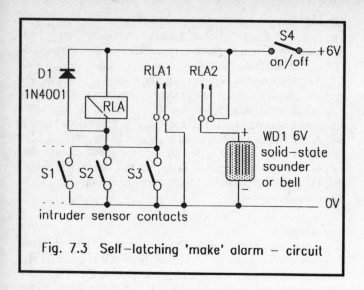

Fig. 7.3 Self–latching 'make' alarm – circuit

circuit and hold on the alarm. This simple self-latching 'make' alarm is shown in Figure 7.3. It operates as follows. When a switch (S1 – S3) or similar sensor contact is 'made' on unauthorised entry, relay RLA is energised by the current flowing from the 6V battery, via the on/off switch S4.

Relay contacts RLA1 close and as they are in parallel with the sensor contacts S1 – S3, they provide a self-latching current to hold in the relay even if all sensor contacts are now open. At the same time, relay contacts RLA2 'make', and the alarm, WD1, is switched across the 6V battery supply. The alarm will continue to sound until the circuit is switched off by the on/off switch S4. The WD1 sounder must be connected the correct way round; i.e. the positive lead to the +6V rail. A 6V indicator lamp can be connected in parallel with the sounder, or replace it if only a visual alarm is required.

The diode D1 across the coil protects the switches against arcing due to the back e.m.f. of the relay coil at switch-off.

Self-latching 'Break' Alarm

Often it is easier to sense for a break-in with a circuit that uses 'break' contacts or switches. For instance, if a window is a vulnerable entry-point then a strip of foil across a pane gives an automatically open-circuit if the window is broken. Also a series of looped contacts offers more of a fail-safe circuit than one that relies on 'make' contacts. From the self-latching 'break' alarm of Figure 7.4 it can be seen that transistor TR1 has its base strapped to 0V by the normally-closed sensor contacts, so is non-conducting. However, when one of the sensor contacts opens, TR1 will conduct on account of the base current supplied by R1 from the positive rail. The resulting collector current will energise relay RLA and contacts RLA1 and RLA2 will close. As in the previous circuit, RLA1 contacts latch the relay on and RLA2 contacts operate the WD1 sounder or bell circuit. The silicon diode, D1, protects the transistor from the back e.m.f. of the coil.

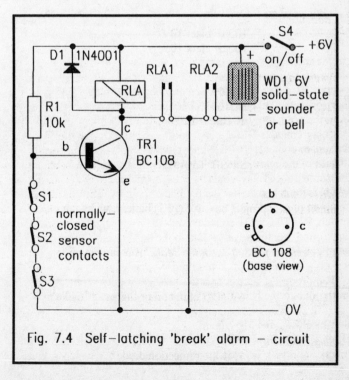

Fig. 7.4 Self—latching 'break' alarm — circuit

Construction

Both these self-latching alarms can be constructed on a small tag strip or terminal block. The layout should pose no problems and will largely depend on the relay used. This should preferably be a 6V version of 185 ohms or more. If a latching version is not essential, then one 'make' contact to energise the sounder will suffice.

Components for Bogus Greenhouse Alarm (Fig. 7.1)

Resistors
R1	1k
R2	22k
R3	22k
R4	1k

Capacitors
C1	100µF elect 10V
C2	100µF elect 10V

Semiconductors
TR1	BC109
TR2	BC109
D1	tri-colour LED

Switches
S1	S.P.S.T. (on/off)

Miscellaneous
Small plastic project box, 9V (PP3) battery, wires, etc.

Components for Self-latching 'Make' Alarm (Fig. 7.3)

Relay
RLA	6V (185 ohm coil or higher, 2 'make' contacts)

Semiconductor
D1	1N4001 protection diode

Sounder
WD1   6V solid-state sounder

Switches
S1–S3   sensor 'make' contacts and switches
S4   S.P.S.T. (on/off)

Components for Self-latching 'Break' Alarm (Fig. 7.4)

Resistors
R1   10k

Relay
RLA   6V (185 ohm coil or higher, 2 'make'
                    contacts)

Semiconductors
TR1   BC108
D1   1N4001 protection diode

Sounder
WD1   6V solid-state

Switches
S1–S3   sensor 'break' strips and switches
S4   S.P.S.T. (on/ff)

Chapter 8

POWER SUPPLIES

Low-Voltage Supplies

As mentioned earlier, the projects described in this book are battery powered, mainly because the active components such as transistors and integrated circuits function satisfactorily on low-voltage supplies, but partly in the interests of safety.

There are of course mains-operated garden gadgets that are commercially available, some are low-voltage types powered by step-down transformers, but these are beyond the scope of this book. Sufficient to say that they should be fitted by a qualified electrician and used in accordance with the maker's instructions.

Primary Batteries

Nowadays, there are bewildering arrays of batteries on display in stores and it is difficult to decide which are the most suitable for a particular circuit.

Power packs specially developed for transistorised equipment are the layer-type batteries where maximum performance is required in minimum space.

The 9V types in order of size and capacity are the PP3, the PP6 and the PP9. A zinc chloride version (PP3S) of the smaller battery has an increased nominal capacity of 0.3Ah (ampere-hours) at 620 ohms for 2 hours per day. At the other end of the scale, the PP9 has a nominal capacity of 4.25Ah at 450 ohms for 4 hours per day. These batteries are suitable for projects that require low current, have intermittent use, or if switched on for long periods have low quiescent currents.

The tubular 1.5V zinc carbon AA (HP7) batteries used in torches have a nominal capacity of 0.4Ah at 3.9 ohms for 1.3 hours per day. For circuits in constant use and those that include relays and motors that demand more current, these are a better solution.

Battery holders are available for connecting up a series of these cells; a four-cell holder is required for a 6V supply, and a six-cell holder for 9V. Ensure that the cells are mounted the right way round; i.e. the positive of one to the negative of the next and so on.

Two of the 4.5V flat batteries (Ever Ready 1289), generally called flashlight batteries, can also be connected in series to provide a high capacity 9V power source. The long flat spring of one should be soldered to the short spring of the other. These are more than adequate for the 9V supplies called for in this book.

Secondary Batteries

For supplying the heavy-duty, low-voltage projects such as garden lighting, electrically-heated propagators, motors, pumps and fans, we need to look further afield.

Lead-acid batteries spring to mind. Car batteries offer a good solution, and discarded spares that lack the starting power demanded by a cold engine on a winter's morning are easy to obtain. If you are also fortunate enough to acquire a solar panel charging system, then your garden can be independent of mains electricity, otherwise you will need a battery charger and a nearby power point. But do remember, although 12V is a low voltage, car batteries pack a lot of power so always fit a fuse and be careful of short-circuits – they could generate a lot of heat!

A General-purpose Power Supply

Dry batteries are an expensive way of powering your low-voltage equipment so if you do acquire an independent 12V car-type battery, you can profitably obtain a 9V or 6V d.c. (direct current) output from it as required.

Circuit

As shown in Figure 8.1, the circuit is simplicity itself. The 12V supply is fed via a 500mA protection fuse FS1 to the on/off switch S1. A light-emitting diode, D1, in series with a current limiting resistor R1, indicates when the circuit is switched on. This serves as a reminder to switch off after use as the circuit draws about 20mA even under no-load conditions. With S1 on, current from the 12V supply flows to the 'in' connection of the 500mA adjustable voltage regulator IC1.

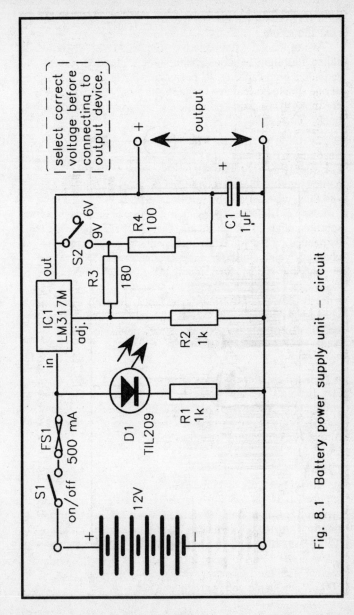

select correct voltage before connecting to output device.

output

Fig. 8.1 Battery power supply unit – circuit

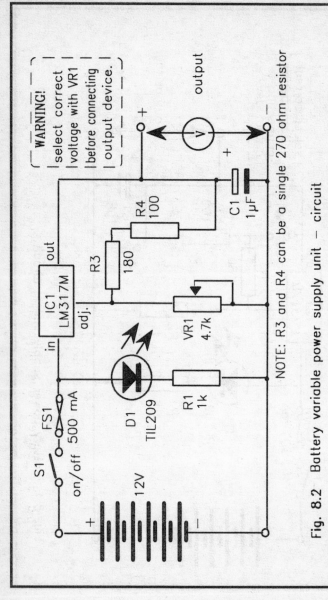

WARNING!
select correct
voltage with VR1
before connecting
output device.

Fig. 8.2 Battery variable power supply unit — circuit

NOTE: R3 and R4 can be a single 270 ohm resistor

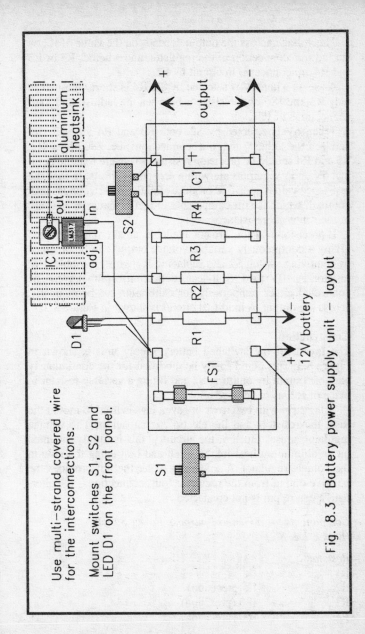

Use multi-strand covered wire for the interconnections.

Mount switches S1, S2 and LED D1 on the front panel.

Fig. 8.3 Battery power supply unit – layout

The voltage across the output depends on the value of R2 on the 'adjust' connection of the regulator, and whether R3 or R3 and R4 are connected in circuit by S2.

As seen, when 9V is selected by S2, R4 is short-circuited so only R3, the 180-ohm resistor is between the 'adjust' and 'out' connections of IC1.

When 6V is selected by S2, both R3 and R4 are in series between the 'adjust' and 'out' connections; i.e. 280 ohms. R2, R3 and R4 should be precision resistors to ensure that the nominal 6V and 9V outputs are within acceptable limits. In fact, the resistance values specified produce slightly lower voltages than nominal, which is still comparable to that of batteries because of their internal resistance.

If precision resistors are not available, an alternative method giving a continuously variable voltage output can be obtained by removing switch S2 and replacing R2 with a variable 4.7k resistor. A 10V f.s.d. (full-scale deflection) voltmeter can be connected either temporarily for calibration, or permanently, across the output. A modified circuit is shown in Figure 8.2.

Construction

The layout of the switched battery supply unit is shown in Figure 8.3. This could easily be modified for the continuously variable output by omitting S2 and fitting a variable resistor in place of R2, as mentioned above.

A tag strip with two rows of seven tags is used to mount the fuse, the resistors and the electrolytic capacitor. The voltage regulator houses much of the circuitry; this is tightly mounted on an aluminium heatsink by a nut and bolt using the hole in the voltage regulator. A solder tag under the nut provides the positive output from the regulator 'out' connection – the alternative centre pin is not connected.

Components for a General-purpose Power Supply (Figs 8.1 & 8.2)

Resistors

R1	1k
R2	1k (precision)
R3	180 (precision)
R4	100 (precision)

Potentiometers
VR1   4.7k (variable version only, replaces R2)

Capacitors
C1   1μF elect 16V

Semiconductors
IC1   LM317M, 500mA adjustable voltage
               regulator
D1   TIL209 light-emitting diode

Switches
S1   S.P.S.T.
S2   S.P.S.T.   (omit for variable version)

Miscellaneous
Tagboard (see text), aluminium plate for heatsink, small plastic
project box, a 12V battery supply, wiring, etc.

Chapter 9

DUSK/DAWN SENSING

Monitoring Activity

Dusk and dawn are both important times of the day in a garden that may call for some monitoring activity, even if the gardener is not around. For instance, you may want lights to switch on automatically at dusk and to switch off at dawn, or to switch on a sprinkler to water your prize blooms in the cool of the evening. At dawn you may need a fan to operate, ventilators opening, or maybe just a dulcet tone to announce that it's a beautiful morning!

There are other inputs for a light-dependent switch other than shafts of daylight. For example, an intruder alarm may be switched by a room light or flashlight shining on a sensor such as a light-dependent resistor (l.d.r.) or photo-conductive cell.

Basic Requirements

A simple circuit that will offer all these functions is shown in Figure 9.1. A light-emitting diode can be included to indicate that the sensing device has operated a relay in the output transistor circuit. Wires from the relay contacts are brought out separately to a terminal block where they can be used to switch a battery circuit to power accessories. At dusk, they can switch on such ancillary equipment as security lights, grow-lights, a heater, a water pump, a fan motor, a vent, or simply sound a remote alarm. Most of this equipment can be found in low-voltage versions.

Although relay contacts can be completely isolated, the use of low-voltage equipment is strongly advised for outdoor use, particularly for those inexperienced in mains wiring procedures. For safety reasons, any connection to mains wiring should only be carried out by a skilled electrician, fully aware of the hazards involved.

Light/Dark Detector Circuit

The basic circuit shown in Figure 9.1 consists of an ORP12 light-dependent resistor (l.d.r.), sometimes referred to as a

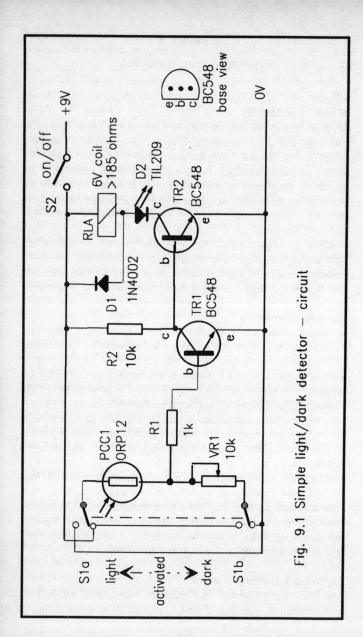

Fig. 9.1 Simple light/dark detector – circuit

66

photo-cell (PCC1), controlling two transistor switching stages that drive a relay. The first stage serves to improve the sensitivity of the circuit.

The changeover switch S1 is an optional extra to include a darkness detector as an alternative to the light detector. It merely changes over the positions of the PCC1 and VR1. As a light-activated detector, the negative rail is switched by S1 to TR1 base via PCC1 instead of via VR1 as shown in the diagram. The variable resistor VR1 and PCC1 form a potential divider across the supply voltage. The resistance of the photocell PCC1 is low when light falls on it, and is high in darkness.

Light-activated: In the 'light-activated' position of S1; i.e. with PCC1 between base and emitter, the variable resistor VR1 is adjusted so that with daylight on PCC1, the voltage amplifier transistor TR1 is just off; i.e. TR2 is switched on, indicated by the LED, D2. If the photo-cell is now covered, to simulate darkness, its resistance increases, the voltage on the base of TR1 rises so that it conducts. Consequently, the low output voltage on TR1 collector is applied to the base of TR2 which switches off the relay and LED in its collector circuit.

Dark-activated: In the 'dark activated' position of S1 (shown in Figure 9.1 with PCC1 between the +9V rail and base), VR1 is re-adjusted so that in darkness, TR1 is just off. This can be simulated by covering the photo-cell if necessary. Transistor TR2 will be on as indicated by D2, which now means that its relay is now activated by darkness.

Uncovering the photo-cell PCC1 in daylight, or if a light shines on it, its resistance will fall and provide sufficient base current for TR1 to conduct and switch off TR2 and its collector load.

Diode D1 across the relay prevents damage to transistor TR2 at switch-off.

The circuit is extremely sensitive around the switch-over point, which may result in some relay 'chatter' at marginal changes in the light. This can be corrected by employing some positive feedback to the input stage. Instead of connecting the positive supply to S1a from the 9V rail connect it from the lower side of the relay coil RLA. Better still, connect a variable resistance across RLA and use the slider to supply the S1a

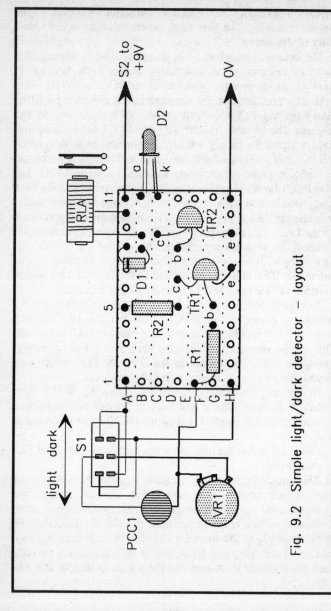

Fig. 9.2 Simple light/dark detector – layout

positive feed. This potentiometer can be adjusted to give a hysteresis gap to improve switch-on and switch-off.

For a permanent dark-activated or light-activated detector, switch S1 can be omitted and the circuit wired accordingly.

Construction
This simple circuit consists of half a dozen components built on a small piece of stripboard (Figure 9.2). There are only 20 solder points on the layout and these are clearly indicated on the component side. A small plastic project box can be used to house the other components. The switches S1, S2, the light-dependent resistor PCC1, and the sensitivity control VR1 can be mounted on the front panel.

Components for Light/Dark Detector Circuit (Fig. 9.1)

Resistors
R1   1k
R2   10k

Potentiometers
VR1   10k

Semiconductors
TR1   BC548 (or BC108)
TR2   BC548 (or BC108)
D1   1N4002 protective diode
D2   TIL209 LED

Switches
S1   slider (double-pole changeover)
S2   S.P.S.T. (on/off)

Relay
RLA   6V coil (185 ohms or more)

Miscellaneous
Small plastic project box, stripboard (7 strips × 11 holes), 9V battery, multi-strand covered connecting wire, etc.

Chapter 10

SEED PROPAGATORS

If you haven't a greenhouse then an electrically-heated propagator can be the next best thing. If you have a greenhouse, then a propagator is an added bonus, greatly enhancing its value. Yes! it can save you money. No need to buy plants that you can grow from seed. A busy seed germination bed can add a month or more to your growing season.

WARNING

Soil-warming cables are ideal for a propagator, and although they are commercially available completely sealed to a 3-pin mains plug, it is not advisable to fit one in a home-made propagator unless you are a qualified electrician. Even if you invest in a commercially-produced propagator, with all electrical fittings, for safety, it should be isolated with a residual current device, a circuit breaker that disconnects in the event of a fault condition. Never work on the mains power supply unless you are certain you know what you are doing.

Basic Propagators

Commercial propagators come in various forms, but basically they consist of a base and a transparent cover to keep the seedlings warm and humid. They are usually moulded plastic covers with some form of ventilation. Home-made propagators are often covered with clear plastic sheeting stretched over a frame as shown in Figure 10.1. A sheet of bubble plastic is ideal at the front as it can be easily rolled back for access to the plants. When subjected to strong sunlight some means of shading for the propagator cover would be necessary to protect the seedlings.

The base tray can be of plywood or aluminium, about 9-in deep with drainage holes in the bottom.

Warming Cables

A layer of polystyrene sheet covered with plastic is fitted below

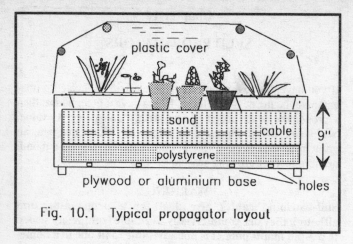

plastic cover

sand

cable

9"

polystyrene

plywood or aluminium base

holes

Fig. 10.1 Typical propagator layout

a six-inch layer of sand that carries the warming cable.

A 75-watt cable evenly spread out about 4 inches below the surface of the sand will adequately heat an area of about 30 × 30 inches. Care should be taken that the cable is evenly spaced with no overlaps. The length of a 75-watt cable, quoted in a recent gardening publication is about 20 feet (6 metres) long. It also states that if twice the area needs to be warmed, then a cable of length of 12 metres is required with an electrical rating of 150 watts. This is true of course, but it is worth pointing out that this isn't as straightforward as it seems. A little thought will show that doubling the length, i.e. doubling the resistance of the cable, will in fact result in half the current and half the power. Although perhaps of little practical use for commercial warming cables, because they are made up to fixed lengths, the calculations are of interest in Figure 10.2. As shown, the higher power rating of 150 watts is obtained by parallel connection of two 6-metre lengths when required to warm double the area.

Some of the commercial soil-warming cables come complete with a thermostat to control the temperature limits.

If you can prevail on an experienced electrician to fit one of these it would be well worthwhile.

Unheated Propagators

You could try your hand at making an unheated propagator in

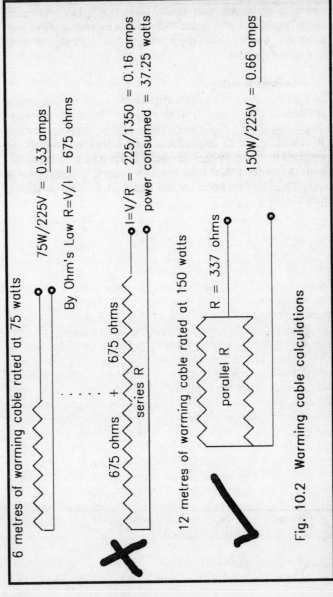

6 metres of warming cable rated at 75 watts

75W/225V = 0.33 amps

By Ohm's Law R=V/I = 675 ohms

675 ohms + 675 ohms
series R

I=V/R = 225/1350 = 0.16 amps
power consumed = 37.25 watts

12 metres of warming cable rated at 150 watts

parallel R   R = 337 ohms

150W/225V = 0.66 amps

Fig. 10.2 Warming cable calculations

73

which to germinate your seeds. However, it has little merit except that if it is well-made, it could be a more acceptable container for your seed trays if you want to take advantage of some of the heat indoors.

Low-Voltage Heating

Low-voltage heating equipment and cable is advertised, but the problem is that to get 75 watts of power from a low-voltage supply, say from a 12V battery, you would be drawing a current of $75W/12V = 6.25$ amps. Some form of intermittent heating supplied by a battery may be useful to keep an area moderately frost-free for a short time, but your battery, depending on its capacity in ampere-hours, would flatten, if the cold conditions persisted.

Chapter 11

SIMPLE INTERCOM

An intercom between house and garden shed can be a useful means of contact. It can relay the ring of the doorbell, telephone calls or perhaps more importantly, inform the preoccupied gardener when it's mealtime.

Loudspeakers are switched for both inputs and outputs and amplification is provided by an integrated circuit.

Two changeover switches, one at each end of the link, are used as press-to-talk controls. When not activated, they revert to the 'listen' mode.

The Intercom Circuit

The heart of the circuit, Figure 11.1, is a general-purpose, low-voltage amplifier, the LM386. This chip can operate from a battery supply of 4.5V to 12V and draws a quiescent current of only 6mA. The voltage gain of the amplifier is controlled internally to 20 (26dB), but a 10μF capacitor C1 connected across pins 1 and 8 increases this to 200 (46dB). Any gain between these two values can be obtained by connecting a resistor in series with C1. For instance, a 1k resistor wired in series with C1 would reduce this gain to about 50.

Capacitor C5 serves as a decoupler for the supply line to prevent instability. Potentiometer VR1, connected to the amplifier input via R1, controls the volume from whichever speaker is switched to the press-to-talk mode.

Construction

The circuit can be mounted on a small piece of stripboard as shown in Figure 11.2. The size of the stripboard could easily be reduced as there are only a few components, but there is little to be gained as the loudspeaker will dictate the size of the unit. Remember to make four breaks in the tracks on the underside of the stripboard, between the opposite pins of the LM386. To prevent instability, the connecting leads should be kept as short as possible. Twist the supply leads together tightly. Also twist

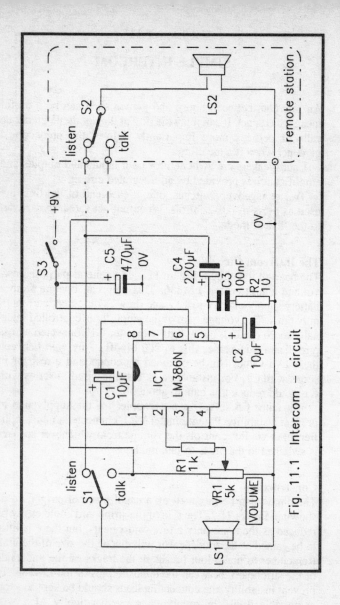

Fig. 11.1 Intercom - circuit

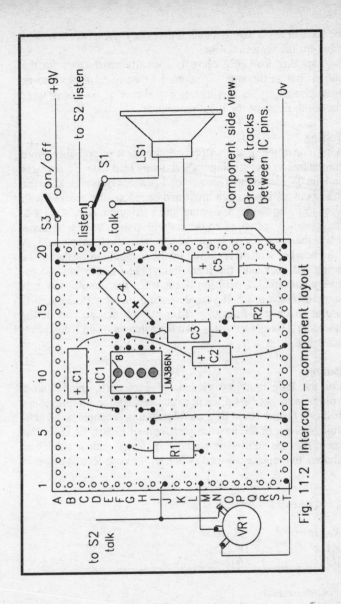

Fig. 11.2 Intercom — component layout

77

the speaker leads together and, if necessary, use a twin screened cable for the remote station.

A speaker load of 8 ohms is normally satisfactory for the output, but as the small speakers LS1 and LS2 serve also as microphones, types having an impedance of 64 ohms were chosen to improve the input matching.

Testing

After constructing the stripboard circuit, it is probably more convenient to test it using a short 3-way lead from S1 contacts and the 0V line to the 'remote' loudspeaker. However, keep the loudspeakers far enough apart and/or reduce the volume with VR1 to avoid the circuit going into oscillation. Acoustic feedback, as it is called, often occurs with public address systems when the microphone is allowed to 'see' the loudspeakers. A loud howl or whistle is caused by the output loudspeaker noise being fed back into the input microphone and being successively amplified. It will not occur when the remote station is some distance away. If you are testing the system alone, it is useful to have a transistor radio playing at one end of the intercom – wedge the press-to-talk switch on – and listen at the other end.

Buzzers

For the long rambling garden (or gardener!), the intercom volume may not be sufficient to attract attention. In this case, a bell or a buzzer could be a useful addition. A simple buzzer circuit is given in the next chapter (part of Figure 12.1). In this case, use the solid-state sounder in series with a battery as shown, but replace the reed switch with a push-to-make switch.

Components for Intercom Circuit (Fig. 11.1)

Resistors
R1   1k
R2   10 ohms

Potentiometers
VR1   5k with switch (S3)

Capacitors

C1	10µF elect 10V wkg. (see text)
C2	10µF elect 10V wkg.
C3	100nF
C4	220µF elect 10V wkg.
C5	470µF elect 10V wkg.

Semiconductor

IC1	LM386N

Switches

S1	changeover non-locking
S2	changeover non-locking
S3	S.P.S.T. (or in VR1)

Loudspeakers

LS1	30–64 ohms miniature
LS2	30–64 ohms miniature

Miscellaneous

Two suitable plastic boxes; stripboard (20 strips × 20 holes); 9V battery and clip, connecting wire, solder, etc.

Chapter 12

WATER BUTT LEVEL ALARMS

When your plants are relying on sustenance from your water butt, it can be a minor disaster if the water runs dry. How can you ensure that a supply of water is available, apart from peering inside that inaccessible tank several times a day? A water-level indicator is the obvious answer.

Again, as in so many of the alarm systems described, once you have established the cause under scrutiny you can choose a suitable sensor, a circuit process and an output device. In this case, the cause is a change in the water level. There are several ways in which this can be sensed.

Magnetic Reed Switch Alarm

If the water butt is made of plastic, then a floating magnet can be used to monitor a predetermined low-level mark by activating an adjacent reed switch on the side of the butt. The principle is shown in Figure 12.1. The magnet is inserted in a cork to keep it floating on the surface. To ensure that the reed switch contacts are in proximity with the magnetic field, the cork is mounted in a length of open-ended plastic tubing fixed down the inside of the water butt. If the water butt is made of magnetic material, the reed switch will need to be inside and could be attached to the outside of the plastic tubing at the minimum water level permitted. However, this means that the contacts to the reed switch need to be well insulated, otherwise the alarm circuit may be activated by water conductivity. If necessary, the reed switch and its leads could be inserted in a thin rubber or plastic tube to keep out the water.

So far, we have a reed switch contact that will close when the water level drops. In its simplest form, the alarm circuit can be a solid-state sounder as shown, or an electric bell, in series with the reed switch and a battery. If a visual indication is preferred to an audible alarm, then replace the sounder with a 6V lamp or an LED with a limiting resistor in series. Using a 6V supply, since an LED drops about 2V at 10mA, the resistor would have to drop 4V at 10mA; i.e. 4V/0.01A = 400 ohms. A

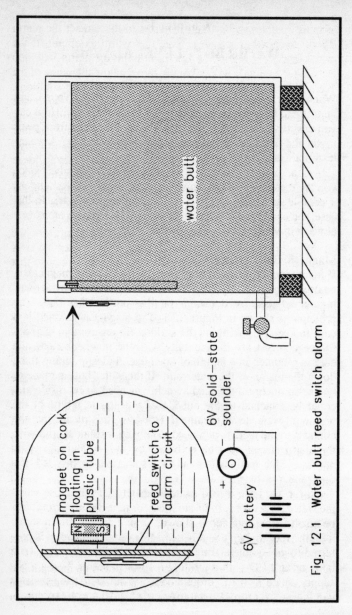

Fig. 12.1 Water butt reed switch alarm

manual switch can be fitted in series to disconnect the alarm circuit once it has sounded. Note that with this circuit, if the water level falls below the low-limit point the alarm will stop because the magnet will gradually move below the range of the reed switch. Fortunately, there are several easy solutions. Firstly, the plastic tube can be restricted immediately opposite the reed switch by drilling a small hole in it and fitting a stop-pin to prevent the cork falling any further. Secondly, another reed switch can be paralleled with the first, located a little lower down so that you get a second warning – rather like a snooze button on a radio alarm! – to remind you that the water is not going to last forever. Alternatively, you can replace the sounder with a relay and use one of the contacts to self-latch the circuit, see Chapter 7 (Fig. 7.3, Self-latching 'make' alarm).

The circuit could include a manual switch to prevent the alarm sounding for long periods. After the water level is restored, it is important to remember to reset the circuit so that the alarm will again be activated when the low level is reached.

Mercury Tilt Switch Alarm

The water level in a tank or water butt can be sensed by the traditional household plumbing method using a plastic ball that floats on the surface of the water, supported by a pivoted arm. Normally, in a cistern this controls the water inlet valve, but for horticultural purposes a mercury tilt switch is attached to the arm (Figure 12.2). The angle of this switch is so arranged that as the ball drops to the 'low-water mark' the switch tilts sufficiently so that the mercury inside the glass tube bridges two contacts. Two leads connected to the circuit (as in Figure 12.1) operate the sounder. With this sensor, the alarm continues until the water level is restored or the circuit is manually switched off. If your tank is supplied from a water main, a conventional ball-cock with inlet valve could be fitted.

Water Butt Alarm Circuit

Finally, Figure 12.3 shows an electronic water butt alarm circuit adapted from the automatic plant waterer circuit of Chapter 4. In fact, your water butt alarm could be incorporated in the circuit of Figure 4.1 by adding the probes in series with the existing probes, and adjusting VR1 (or shielding PCC1) so

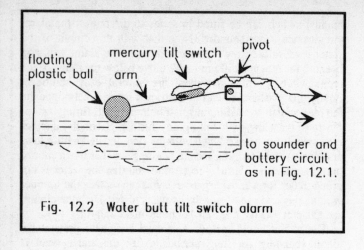

Fig. 12.2 Water butt tilt switch alarm

that input IC1 pin 1 is high, irrespective of the ambient light.

The water butt alarm circuit is formed by two CMOS inverter gates, IC1, in cascade, driving a transistor output stage. The conductivity of the water is sensed by two copper rods suspended to a depth estimated to be the alarm 'on' level required. The sensitivity control VR1, and the resistance of the water bridging the probes, form a potential divider across the supply rails. This holds inputs 1 and 2 of the first inverter gate IC1 low, providing the resistance of VR1 is set sufficiently high. The logic low input on this inverter gives a high output on pin 3. In turn the high input on pins 5 and 6 is inverted to give a low on IC1, output pin 4. Consequently, transistor TR1 is non-conducting and the alarm is inactive.

However, when the water level falls below the probes, the gate input is disconnected from the 0V line and sufficient current flows via VR1 to make input pins 1 and 2 go high. In turn, output pin 3 goes low, which, via the second inverter gives a high output on pin 4. Base current is applied via R1 to switch on TR1 and the collector current activates the solid-state sounder and lights the LED, D1. The alarm conditions continue until the water level is restored, or S1 is switched off.

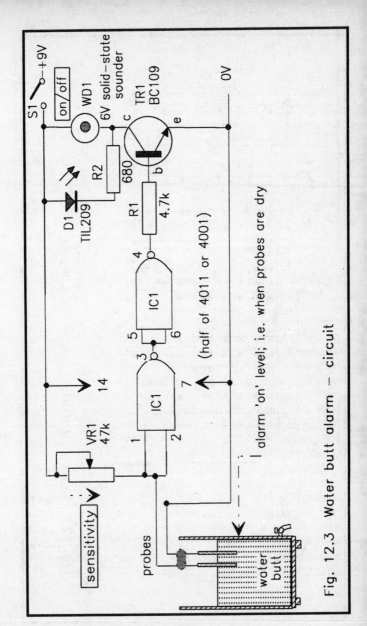

Fig. 12.3 Water butt alarm – circuit

85

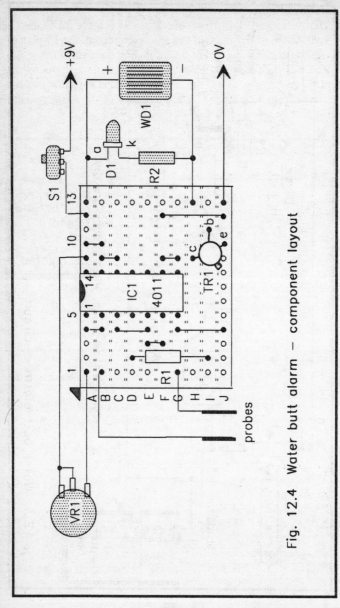

Fig. 12.4 Water butt alarm – component layout

86

Construction

The water-butt alarm component layout (Figure 12.4) uses a small piece of 0.1-in matrix stripboard to match the 14 pins of integrated circuit, IC1. The layout mainly consists of mounting the chip, soldering in the straps and interconnections to the panel-mounted components. The extra straps not shown on the circuit diagram are used to tie the inputs of the spare gates to the supply rails to avoid instability.

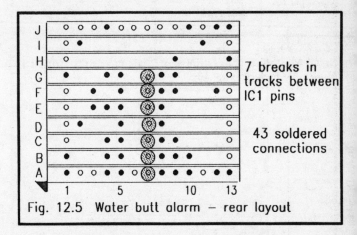

Fig. 12.5 Water butt alarm — rear layout

Figure 12.5 shows the solder points and track breaks on the rear layout.

A small ABS plastic project box can be used to house the stripboard, switch S1, VR1, D1, WD1 and 9V battery.

Components for Water Butt Alarm Circuit (Fig. 12.3)

Resistors
R1   4.7k
R2   680 ohms

Potentiometers
VR1   47k

87

Semiconductors
IC1	4011
TR1	BC109
D1	LED, TIL209

Sounder
WD1	6V solid-state

Switches
S1	S.P.S.T.

Miscellaneous
Small ABS project box, stripboard 0.1-in matrix (10 strips × 13 holes), 9V battery, wire, etc.

Chapter 13

PROCESS TIMER

A timer is a useful accessory for the ardent gardener. Time has a habit of standing still when you're absorbed in some fascinating interest that holds your attention. Apart from a timely reminder that one has a home to go to, there are a number of processes in the garden that may call for a pre-determined time to be set: time to water the pot plants, time to shade the greenhouse, time to check the temperatures, etc.

In this design, after that time has elapsed, it is arranged that a relay will be released and a buzzer can sound. Relay contacts can of course be used to activate or release other circuits such as heaters, sprinklers, lights, etc. To cover a large timing interval, on one variable control, the time can be switched between seconds and minutes.

The circuit for this timer, Figure 13.1, is based on the popular timer integrated circuit 555. For this purpose, it is wired to operate in its monostable mode. This is sometimes called a 'one-shot' because after triggering it produces a single rectangular-wave of pre-determined length and then resets to await further triggering. The timing depends on the choice of an electrolytic capacitor charging through a resistor. Capacitors C1 and C2 are switched into circuit when the interval required is in seconds, and C3 is switched in when the interval required is in minutes. Variable resistor VR1 covers the two ranges. The duration of the output pulse, known as the quasi-stable time, is determined by the relationship:

$$\text{Time} = 1.1 \times R \times C \text{ seconds}$$

(where R is in ohms and C is in farads). So with $R = 2M$ and $C = 1000\mu F$, the largest time interval would be:

$$\text{Time} = 1.1 \times 2,000,000 \times 0.001 \text{ seconds} = 36 \text{ mins approx.}$$

After switch-on, pressing S2 momentarily, actuates the relay RLA and starts the timing cycle by charging the capacitor, C1

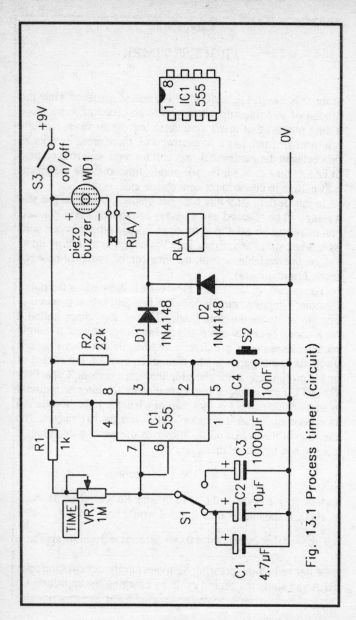

Fig. 13.1 Process timer (circuit)

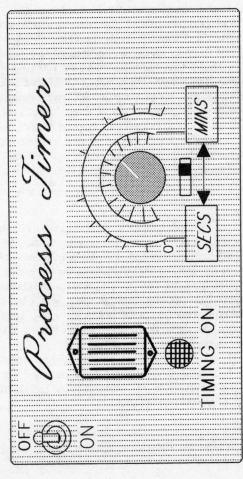

Calibrate scale according to requirements
against second or minute hand of clock.

Fig. 13.2 Process timer (front panel)

+ C2, or C3, exponentially via VR1 and R1 from the 9V line. When the capacitor has charged to two-thirds the supply voltage, pins 3, 7 and 6 are pulled to zero. Relay RLA releases and the solid-state buzzer is energised via RLA/1 contacts from the supply rails. D1 and D2 protect against the coil back EMF. The values of the timing components can be chosen to suit your own requirements. For instance, if you want to obtain similar scales for seconds and minutes divide the value of the larger capacitor C3 by sixty to calculate the smaller one required (approximately 16µF). On experiment, with the 1000µF capacitor a fixed value of resistance 27k in place of VR1 gave a delay of about half a minute; 100k in place of VR1 gave a delay of 2 minutes; 560k gave 11 minutes; and a fixed resistance of 2 megohms (tolerance unknown) gave an elapsed time of nearly an hour. Use a clock or watch with a second hand or digital indication to calibrate the time scale when satisfied that the controls are suitable. A typical front panel layout is given in Figure 13.2.

Construction

The layout (Figure 13.3) is built on a small stripboard (15 strips × 14 holes), matrix 0.1-in to match the pinning of the 555 IC. The components are not crowded, and the only breaks in the copper strips are the four between the pins of the integrated circuit, and between the relay coil pins, shown on the underside layout diagram. The pinning for the relay will obviously depend on the type used. Be careful not to leave any whiskers of copper when you make the break, as fault-finding due to short-circuits can be very time-consuming!

A small ABS plastic project box can be used to house the components. The solid-state buzzer can be mounted on the front panel with the controls, or behind it as preferred; make sure you observe the correct polarity.

Components for Process Timer (Fig. 13.1)

Resistors
R1   1k
R2   22k

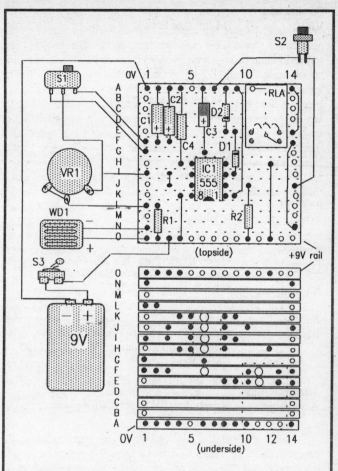

The layout of the components and connections
shown on the topside of the stripboard. Notice
the breaks to be made in the copper strip
between the IC pins, and between the relay
connections on the underside; also the solder
points.

Fig. 13.3 Process timer — layout

93

Potentiometers
VR1   1M lin. (see text)

Capacitors
C1   4.7µF 16V (see text)
C2   10µF 16V (see text)
C3   1000µF 16V (see text)
C4   10nF plastic foil

Semiconductors
IC1   NE 555N
D1, D2   IN4148 (2 off)

Sounder
WD1   solid-state buzzer

Switches
S1   slider, single-pole changeover
S2   push-to-make (non-locking)
S3   S.P.S.T. (timer on/off)

Relay
RLA   6V relay with break contact (example:
                  Maplin Ultra Miniature 6V S.P.D.T. type
                  FM91Y)

Miscellaneous
ABS project box, stripboard, 9V battery, wiring, etc.

Chapter 14

ELECTRONIC SCARECROW

To feed the birds can be most commendable, but to give them the biggest bite of the cherry, strawberry, freshly sown seed, or whatever takes their fancy in your vegetable garden is sheer extravagance. Traditionally, the conventional scarecrow is the worst-dressed Englishman in a field, but recently Anglia TV reported that after lengthy research, two large plastic owls had been procured in Ipswich to scare away hordes of pigeons that were 'decorating' municipal buildings. On the other hand, a farmer friend told me about a scarecrow economy pack that consisted of bottles set in the ground and partially filled with water. The wind, blowing free of charge across the tops of the bottles, produces rushing sounds at different frequencies depending on the water levels, which reportedly scares away the birds. Besides the birds, bees, moles, mice, rats and rabbits, it's also true that even the best of pets can become pests in a garden.

Admittedly, the electronic scarecrow circuit to be described does not look like a bird of prey, but if it was housed in a plastic owl instead of a plastic project box it might increase the 'scare factor'!

Principle
The electronic scarecrow is based on the principle that birds and pests find varying high-pitched sounds unpleasant. The active circuit blocks of this unit are two oscillators, a slow one modulating a faster one to generate a warbling high frequency sound.

Circuit
Two separate 555 timer circuits are used for the oscillators as shown in Figure 14.1. The first timer, IC1 together with its associated components is wired as a low frequency oscillator, controlled by VR1. This operates at about 7–10Hz, the frequency dependent on C1 and the setting of VR1. As R1 is fairly large, the charge and discharge times are comparable, so

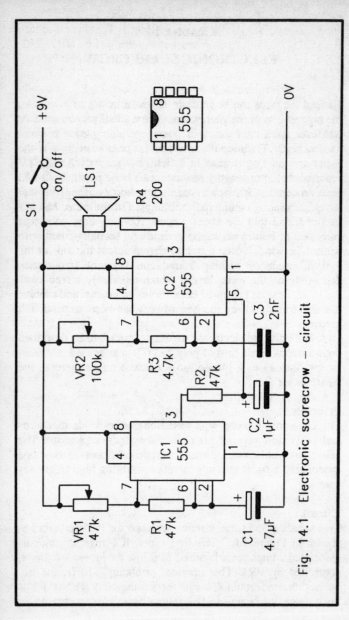

Fig. 14.1 Electronic scarecrow – circuit

giving a triangular waveform at output pin 3. The second timer circuit, IC2, oscillates at a frequency determined by VR2, R3, C3 and the voltage fed to control input 5, from IC1, pin 3, via R2, C2.

It is worth experimenting with the values of R2, C2 and adjusting the two variable controls to get the best warble effect. The prototype experimental circuit used a small piezo sounder in the output with a resonant frequency of about 4kHz and an impedance of 500 ohms. This gave a high-pitched two-tone whistling sound that could be heard towards the top of the audio frequency range and seemed reasonably effective at close encounters of the bird-kind. A small tweeter loudspeaker was tried and this was considerably louder, at least to the ears of mere mortals!

If a permanent tone is required instead of the odd manually-operated burst of sound, then it is more pleasant to the human ear if the frequency control VR2 is adjusted so that the output is above the audio range (20kHz or more). Many animals can hear sounds perfectly well in this ultrasonic range, beyond our hearing range. In this case, a piezo tweeter is recommended, or an ultrasonic transducer with an amplified output stage. Ultrasonic transducers act like a capacitor, the plate flexing at very fast frequencies around 40kHz.

Construction

The circuit is built on a stripboard layout (Figure 14.2) around the two 555 timer chips, IC1 and IC2. The only other components mounted on the stripboard are three resistors and three capacitors. The remaining controls can be affixed to the front panel of a plastic project box, owl-shaped or otherwise!

Components for Electronic Scarecrow (Fig. 14.1)

Resistors

R1	47k
R2	47k
R3	4.7k
R4	200 ohms

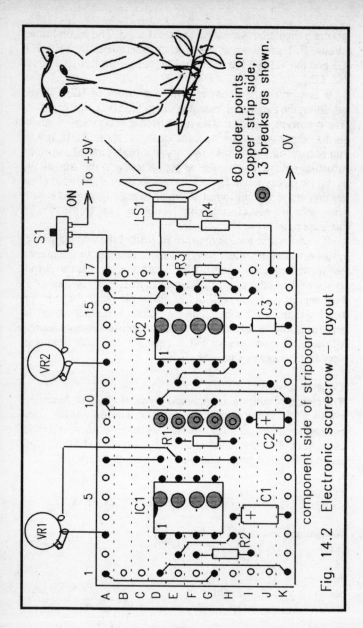

To +9V

ON

S1

LS1

R4

60 solder points on copper strip side, 13 breaks as shown.

0V

17

R3

15

IC2

C3

1

VR2

10

R1

C2

5

IC1

C1

VR1

R2

1

A B C D E F G H I J K

component side of stripboard

Fig. 14.2 Electronic scarecrow – layout

98

Potentiometers
VR1   47k
VR2   100k

Capacitors
C1   4.7µF elect 10V
C2   1µF elect 10V
C3   2nF

Semiconductors
IC1   555 timer
IC2   555 timer

Sounder
LS1   Piezo sounder (see text)

Switches
S1   S.P.S.T. (on/off)

Miscellaneous
Plastic project box, stripboard 0.1-in matrix, 11 strips × 17 holes, 9V battery, wiring, etc.

Chapter 15

A pH METER

The answer lies in the soil . . .

It's common knowledge that the condition of your soil is an important factor if you want strong, healthy plants. To keep plants happy – invest in a pH meter, or why not make your own? In scientific terms, a pH meter measures the percentage of electrified hydrogen atoms present in the soil. In layman's terms it can tell you whether your soil is alkaline or acidic. Actually, pH stands for percentage hydrogen!

The meter probe, or probes, should be inserted into previously moistened soil to take a reading. A pH meter reading of 7 indicates that the soil is neutral, neither alkaline nor acidic. Alkalinity is present in the soil if the reading is 7.5 or more; acidity is present for readings less than 5.5.

If alkalinity occurs then the remedy is to add sulphate of ammonia to neutralise it. Conversely, if a soil is too acidic, then it needs an application of lime to neutralise it, or to make it alkaline. For the vegetable garden, a pH between 5.5 and 7.5 is generally preferred; shrubs thrive on 5.5 to 7.0, the neutral figure. Suitable pH levels for fruit-growing cover a more varied range. Fortunately, this information is widely available in the popular gardening handbooks and magazines.

. . . and in the water!

Besides harmful levels of chlorine and sudden changes of temperature that can occur when adding large amounts of tap water to replenish a pond in summer, fish are not very happy with extremes of pH factor; i.e. water gardens that are too alkaline or too acid. Usually, fish and aquatic plantlife can thrive without problem in a range of pH between 6.5 and 8.5 – outside these limits they will suffer!

Alkalinity is more common than acidity and a pH of 9.0 or more is often caused by water running into a pond over concrete paths; the answer is to seal all exposed concrete surfaces. As mentioned, acid water is less of a problem, but it's worth noting that water running in from peaty soil could push the pH

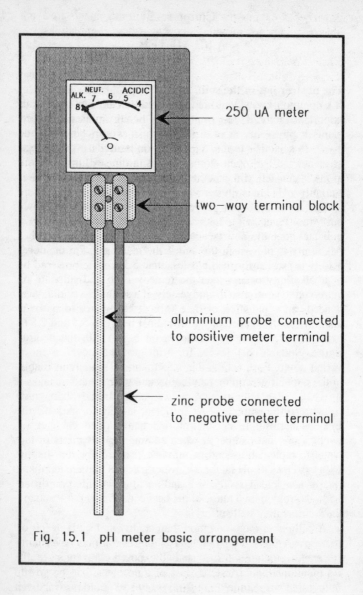

Fig. 15.1 pH meter basic arrangement

down below 6.0 into the acid region. Buffering agents are available from aquatics suppliers to counter these eventualities.

Basic Arrangement of pH Meter

The idea of the pH meter is very simple. It depends on the basis that two dissimilar metals immersed in an electrolyte (an electrically conductive liquid) forms a simple cell. For instance if we use zinc as the negative electrode and aluminium as the positive electrode, then different voltages can be measured between these electrodes depending on the type of electrolyte used. If the electrolyte is a salty solution the voltage is about 0.25V. However, if the electrolyte is acidic, then the voltage is about 0.4V. This variation in voltage depending on the nature of the electrolyte suggests the idea for our pH meter. As shown in Figure 15.1, for the basic arrangement we need two probes, one of aluminium coupled to the positive terminal of a microammeter, and another probe of zinc coupled to the negative terminal of the meter. The meter is of course powered by the simple cell formed when the probes are pushed into the electrolyte, in this case the moistened earth. And the answer does lie in the soil! The meter will be deflected according to the measure of the acidity of the soil under test.

Calibrating

Although it's easy to make up a pH meter – the circuit is self-explanatory from the arrangement of Figure 15.1 – it takes a little longer to calibrate it. If you want to use it as a rough guide to pH conditions, it may be sufficient merely to mark-off the three states, 'alkaline', 'neutral' and 'acidic'.

However, if you can borrow a commercial pH meter from a friend, or if you acquire one of the reasonably-priced pH kits (non-electronic) displayed in superstores and garden centres, it is fairly easy to compare results and mark off your scale accordingly.

Electrolyte

You'll need quite a range of electrolytes and it may be easier to look nearer to home for it than in the garden. You can use table salt dissolved in water, squeeze a lemon, or use powdered citric acid. I found that a small measure of malt vinegar from the kitchen cupboard worked well! For instance, in this solution, with my makeshift probes, a thick aluminium rod and the hollowed out zinc casing of an AAA cell, I measured a current flow of 200 microamps and a voltage of 0.4V. The current was rather more than that measured on a commercial pH meter as the size of the electrodes, spacing between them, and depth in the electrolyte, affected the reading; adjustments can easily be made.

It is interesting to note that if copper is used instead of aluminium, a higher voltage reading is obtained. For the acidic electrolyte, a potential difference of almost 1V was obtained; in contrast, the salt solution registered about 0.75V. This seems to suggest that copper and zinc electrodes could well be used as probes for a simple moisture meter (see also Chapter 20).

Heavy-duty mains cable provides a fruitful source of copper wire, if you wish to use this as an alternative to aluminium for further moisture experiments.

Construction

The moving coil meter used was a 1.5-in square-faced signal VU meter with a sensitivity of 250µA full-scale deflection, but other suitable meters can be pressed into service if available. To protect the meter and its terminals it can be mounted on a small project box together with the two-way terminal block that supports the probe electrodes. If aluminium rod is not readily available, a narrow strip (say, three-sixteenths of an inch) can be cut from a six-inch length of aluminium. Zinc can also be obtained from a hardware shop, and may be commonly obtained in the form of a galvanised nail.

The alternative arrangement shown in Figure 15.2 uses a single concentric probe. Here, as mentioned, the zinc rod was the outer casing of an old AAA-size cell that had been drilled out to form a tube. A push-fit plastic tube was inserted to act as an insulating sleeve between the central aluminium rod and the zinc outer casing.

If the aluminium rod is extended, it could be used as the fixing to the meter support; otherwise use flexible leads from the probe to the meter.

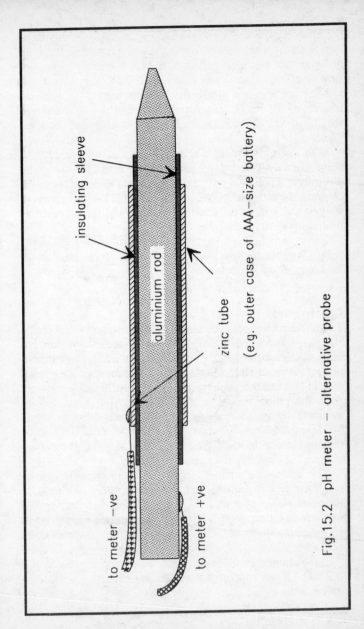

insulating sleeve

aluminium rod

zinc tube
(e.g. outer case of AAA-size battery)

to meter −ve

to meter +ve

Fig.15.2 pH meter – alternative probe

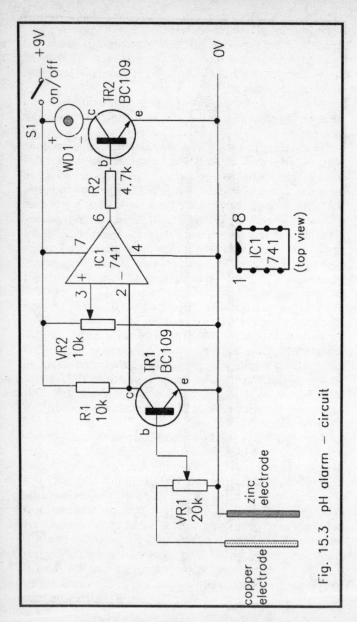

Fig. 15.3 pH alarm – circuit

106

Experimental pH Alarm

Apart from the hand-held pH meter described, if ponds and water gardens are your scene then you may think about devising an alarm circuit that will warn you if your pond-water pH strays outside limits.

As mentioned, if your garden happens to be on the edge of a peat bog there is a chance that acid water might be the major problem.

The circuit of Figure 15.3 is arranged to raise an alarm if the water is excessively acidic. The circuit senses the voltage difference between the copper and zinc electrodes immersed in the water and applies this voltage across the potentiometer VR1. The slider is set to pick off a voltage slightly less than 0.7V so that transistor TR1 is just off. This voltage is readily available with this copper-zinc combination around about the neutral point. Potentiometer VR2 sets the voltage reference level on pin 3 of op-amp IC1 which is used as an inverting comparator. The reference level is adjusted to a value below that of the signal input pin 2, which is high when TR1 is not conducting. Under these conditions the output, pin 6, is held low and TR2 does not conduct. However, when TR1 is switched on by the probe voltage when the pH is excessively acidic, the collector voltage drops and input pin 2 goes negative with respect to the reference voltage on pin 3. Consequently, the output on pin 6 goes high, supplies base current to switch on TR2, and the piezo buzzer WD1 in the collector sounds a warning. This buzzer may be replaced by an LED (anode to the +9V rail) if a visual indication is sufficient.

To monitor excessive alkalinity, a more likely cause of pollution, we need to use a non-inverting comparator. The output from the probes is smaller when the water is alkaline, so we need to sense the drop in input to TR1. In this case, TR1 will be conducting over the normal pH range and will cease to conduct when alkalinity occurs. To meet these requirements, it is necessary to reverse inputs 2 and 3 to IC1 and to increase the input from VR1 so that over the normal pH range TR1 conducts and cuts out the buzzer. At the point of excessive alkalinity (pH > 8.5, a low input from the copper-zinc probes) the input is insufficient to maintain TR1 conducting. In this condition, its collector voltage, now connected to pin 3, will exceed the

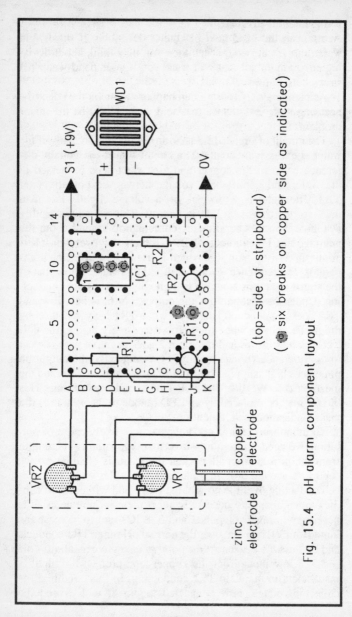

Fig. 15.4 pH alarm component layout

(top-side of stripboard)

(⬢ six breaks on copper side as indicated)

reference voltage connected to pin 2 and the output on pin 6 will go high; transistor TR2 switches on and the alarm sounds.

It must be stressed that this is only suggested as a basis for experiment, and all circuits should be tested thoroughly before being put to practical use. However, the use of different metals for electrodes in pH and moisture measurement does offer some interesting possibilities.

A component layout for the experimental pH alarm is given in Figure 15.4. The stripboard is 0.1-in matrix, 11 strips × 14 holes. The six track breaks on the copper side are as indicated.

Components

pH Meter (Fig. 15.1)
Meter 250μA f.s.d. moving coil meter, order code LB80B, Maplin
2-way terminal block
Aluminium probe (see text)
Zinc probe (see text)

pH Alarm (Fig. 15.3)

Resistors
R1	10k
R2	4.7k
VR1	20k potentiometer
VR2	10k potentiometer

Semiconductors
TR1	BC109
TR2	BC109
IC1	741 op-amp

Sounder
WD1	piezo buzzer

Chapter 16

PONDS AND PUMPS

Your garden pond may be a joy to behold in the summer, when aquatic plants are flourishing and fish are glinting as they dart to and fro in the bright sunshine. Nevertheless, you may not be overly fond of that pond on a dull winter's day when the plants are past their best and the fish look scarcely livelier than they do on the local fishmonger's slab.

Water Movement
It's times like this that a little water movement wouldn't go amiss – a waterfall or a fountain. For these you need a pump! Fortunately, garden centres are stocking a number of low-voltage electrical features, such as submersible pumps and self-contained fountains that are admirably suitable for livening up the water garden. Many of these items are commercially available from superstores. So, with the help of a qualified electrician you could give your pond or pool a more attractive look. Nothing so ambitious as the 300ft-high magnificent, Emperor Fountain at Chatsworth House, but even a modest 4ft spray with a subtle touch of lighting makes a worthwhile feature.

A fountain is easier to install than a waterfall and lends itself more to the formal, suburban pond. Basically, you need a low-voltage, submersible pump and a power supply to suit the voltage rating of the pump motor. If your garden has no mains electricity then you will need a 12V direct current pump motor to operate the fountain from a battery supply. Otherwise, most low-voltage systems are powered from a 12V or 24V supply, generally from indoor standard transformers that step down the mains voltage. Kits are supplied with full instructions, which must be followed carefully, but it is still recommended that a qualified electrician should be consulted.

Low-Voltage Fountain
The layout of a typical low-voltage system for a fountain is illustrated in Figure 16.1. Check that the electrical connections

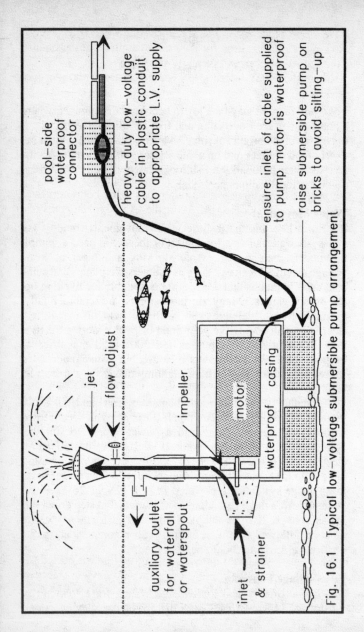

pool-side waterproof connector

heavy-duty low-voltage cable in plastic conduit to appropriate L.V. supply

ensure inlet of cable supplied to pump motor is waterproof

raise submersible pump on bricks to avoid silting-up

jet

flow adjust

impeller

motor

waterproof casing

auxiliary outlet for waterfall or waterspout

inlet & strainer

Fig. 16.1 Typical low-voltage submersible pump arrangement

to the submersible pump are waterproof and that heavy-duty low-voltage cable is used for the entire length from the pump to the low-voltage transformer.

Remember that water and electricity are a dangerous combination!

Usually, the pump cable provides for a connector at the side of the pool to detach the pump for maintenance purposes. This cable and connector should also be completely waterproof. The added value of this pond-side connector is that in the depth of winter, the pump can be disconnected and a low-voltage pond heater substituted to ensure there is no possibility of frozen fish! An odd length or two of drain pipes at the bottom of the pond provide a welcome refuge (for the fish!) in the depths of winter.

Waterfalls

An auxiliary outlet to most pumps could be used to feed a waterspout or waterfall. To supply both a fountain and a waterfall might stretch the pumping capacity of a low-voltage submersible so it might be better to make it an 'or', rather than an 'and/or' function. The fountain jet may be turned off occasionally in favour of the waterfall outlet. Waterfalls are a more natural feature of the country garden, where the water can be encouraged to run over a rocky shelf into a pond. There are many books on water gardens that illustrate the beautiful effects that can be obtained by skilful landscaping. Any of the cable that runs underground should be channelled in plastic conduit, and a record kept of where the cable lies to avoid the chance of any accidents when digging. Only equipment specifically designed for outdoors should be used. Don't forget that a few lights strategically placed around a pond will liven it up at night. Chapter 19 gives some information on lighting circuit arrangements.

WARNING

It must be stressed that no equipment must be connected to the mains without a residual current device (circuit breaker). Never work on the mains power supply unless you are certain you know what you are doing.

113

Chapter 17

SIMPLE ANEMOMETER

"There's no sun up in the sky, stormy weather", so the old song goes, but how stormy is it? A stiff breeze or a howling gale? Do you ever stick a wet thumb in the air and wonder if it's time to batten down the hatches, check the fences or push the bean sticks in a little firmer? A simple anemometer that measures the force of the wind could satisfy your curiosity and also provide a useful addition to your own garden weather centre.

First Thoughts
To measure the wind speed, it is necessary to collect and sense a sample. Windmills have been around for a long time, conveniently converting the linear force of the wind into rotary energy; the commercial anemometer emulates this idea with its small air-collecting cups on the end of rotating arms.

The modern wind generators that produce electricity also provide us with our first thoughts on how to measure wind speed.

Motor-Generator Principle
When the armature of a small direct current motor is rotated it generates a voltage. If we drive the shaft of a small d.c. motor from the anemometer we can get an electrical analogue of wind speed by measuring the voltage produced.

Revolution Counter
An alternative idea to this electric motor principle is to use an electronic solution. We can detect the number of rotations of the anemometer, and hence determine the wind speed with a frequency counter. The number of revolutions can easily be sensed by mounting a small magnet on the rotating arms to operate a reed switch. Pulse signals can then be applied to trigger a frequency meter.

Wind Collector
Whatever the method of measuring you settle for, you will need

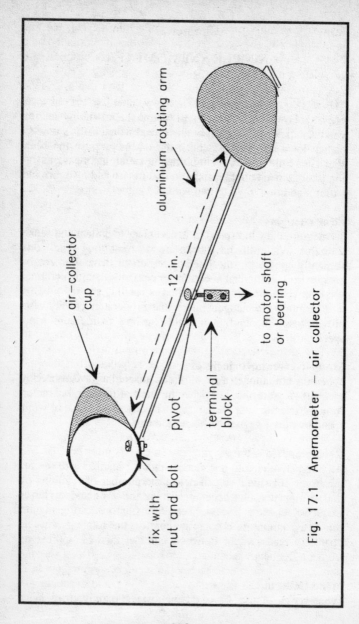

air-collector
cup

aluminium rotating arm

.12 in.

fix with
nut and bolt

pivot

terminal
block

to motor shaft
or bearing

Fig. 17.1 Anemometer – air collector

to make a rotating arm with cups to collect the air. This must be lightweight and able to rotate freely whether it's mounted on a motor shaft or on a fixed bearing. The basic construction of a complete arm is shown in Figure 17.1.

A strip of aluminium about 12 inches long makes a good arm. The two cups can be small cones made from aluminium, or two halves of the plastic eggs that are dispensed by vending machines. These can be fastened on to the ends of the arm, but remember before screwing that they face in opposite directions. After the anemometer is calibrated, the motor or bearing carrying the rotating arm must be attached to a mast at a sufficient height to catch the prevailing wind.

Anemometer Motor-Generator

The layout of the motor generator wind speed indicator is illustrated in Figure 17.2. Circuit-wise it is simply a small d.c. motor coupled to a voltmeter. The shaft of the motor can be attached to the collector arm by means of a single terminal block coupling as shown. The miniature d.c. motor must be able to spin freely. The low-voltage type operated by solar cells are most suitable.

The voltmeter selected should be capable of reading up to 1V full-scale deflection. If you have a multimeter, try it on a low voltage range to get an idea of the output at different wind speeds. A milliammeter can easily be adapted as a voltmeter by including a multiplier resistance in series with it.

Anemometer Frequency Meter Circuit

This circuit counts the revolutions of the air collector and measures them in a frequency meter, based on the popular 555 timer IC. The circuit is given in Figure 17.3. Pulses are produced by a magnet attached to the rotating arm of the air collector, which activates the reed switch, RS1. These negative-going pulses are applied via capacitor C1 to the trigger input pin 2 of the timer, IC1, operating in the monostable mode. The result is that an internal transistor is turned off and so prevents C3 from discharging. The greater the wind speed, the faster the number of pulses and so the output meter reading response is proportional to the frequency. Resistor R5 and capacitor C3 determine the time delay of the monostable output pulses. With

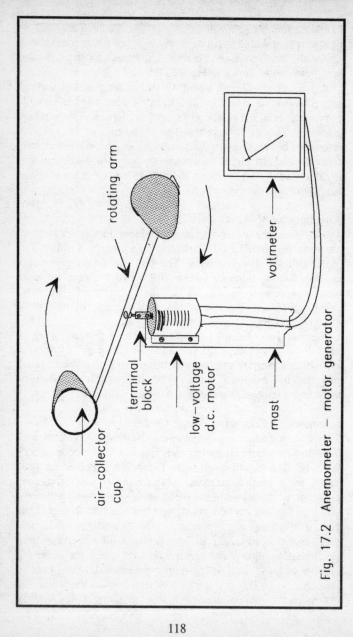

rotating arm

air-collector cup

terminal block

low-voltage d.c. motor

mast

voltmeter

Fig. 17.2 Anemometer – motor generator

118

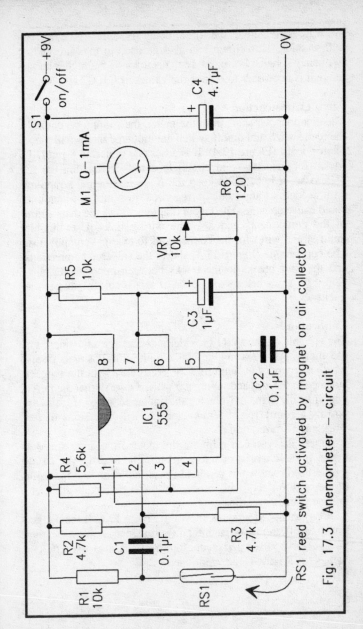

Fig. 17.3 Anemometer – circuit

RS1 reed switch activated by magnet on air collector

119

the values selected, the time delay is approximately 10 milliseconds. This circuit can also be used to measure audio frequency signals. For measurements towards the higher audio range it is necessary to reduce the values of C1, C3 and R5.

Circuit Construction

The components, apart from the meter, the calibration control, the reed switch and on/off switch are mounted on a small piece of stripboard (Figure 17.4). It is advisable to use an 8-pin DIL socket for the integrated circuit to avoid overheating the IC pins. Also, it is better to keep the IC in its original wrapping until needed, as any static during circuit assembly or handling could cause damage. The layout diagram shows the disposition of the components and also the wiring links. Use flexible multi-strand wires for the connections to external components. The copper side (Figure 17.5) shows the soldered connections and the four breaks in the tracks between opposite IC pins. Check for any whiskers of copper, or excess solder between the tracks.

Calibration

The variable resistor VR1 provides a calibration adjustment for the meter. After wiring up the circuit, it is easy to check whether it works by lining up the reed relay with the magnet attached to the arm and giving it a whirl. Observe that the faster you spin the arm, the greater the meter reading. If you can borrow a commercial anemometer this will take some of the work out of calibration.

Otherwise, you can calibrate the meter from a car speedo-meter. In the interests of safety, get a friend to drive you along a little-used road while you hold the air-collector and mast out of the sunshine roof and observe the meter deflection at different speedometer readings.

A typical speed graph is shown in Figure 17.6. If the deflection is insufficient you can mount two magnets as shown so that you get two pulses per revolution. You can also try different values for R5 and C3 as mentioned.

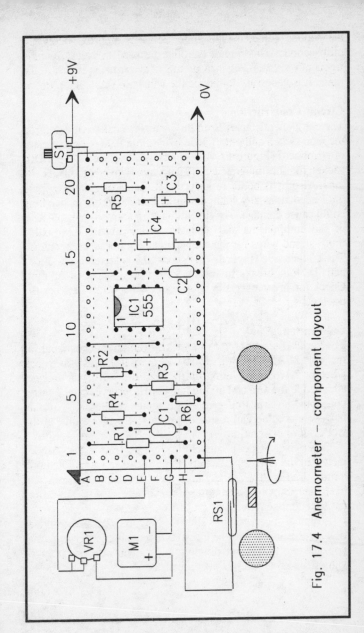

Fig. 17.4 Anemometer — component layout

121

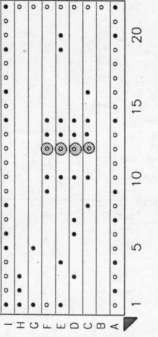

42 soldering points and four breaks under IC1

Fig. 17.5 Anemometer – copper side layout

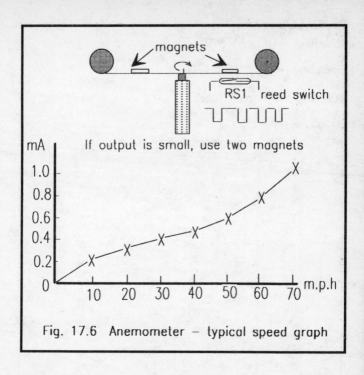

Fig. 17.6 Anemometer — typical speed graph

Components for Simple Anemometer

Resistors

R1, R5	10k (2 off)
R2, R3	4.7k (2 off)
R4	5.6k
R6	120 ohms

Potentiometer

VR1	10k

Capacitors

C1, C2	0.1μF (2 off)
C3	1μF elect 10V
C4	4.7μF elect 10V

123

Semiconductors
IC1   555 timer

Switches
S1   S.P.S.T.
RS1   reed switch

Meter
M1   moving coil 0–1mA (f.s.d.)

Chapter 18

A SIMPLE METAL DETECTOR

Treasure Trove!

Your garden is an ideal starting place to look for buried treasure, even if the only gold you discover is a few goldtop milk bottle caps. Recently a Suffolk farmer, searching for an old hammer, discovered a hoard of coins that experts claim to be the find of the century.

Apart from finding mislaid, rusty tools hidden below the surface, a metal detector is always useful in a garden for locating the runs of water pipes and buried electric cables.

Heterodyning Principle

The simplest detector described is based on the heterodyning principle. As shown in the block diagram of Figure 18.1, two supersonic oscillators are mixed to produce an audio beat signal that varies in pitch as one of the oscillator frequencies is varied by the proximity of a metal object. Sum and difference frequencies between the two radio frequency (r.f.) oscillators are produced. If the two r.f. oscillators are closely tuned, the resultant difference frequencies will give an audio beat note that can be detected and amplified.

To locate the presence of a metal object, a 'search coil' in the shape of a small frame aerial is used in one of the r.f. oscillators. The proximity of the metal object increases the permeability and consequently the inductance of the tuning coil and therefore its frequency. It also has some effect on the capacitance. A frequency of about 900kHz to 1MHz was found to be suitable for both variable and fixed r.f. oscillators.

Circuit

The circuit diagram of Figure 18.2 uses two transistors wired as oscillators and an integrated circuit amplifier. The variable oscillator is formed by transistor circuit TR1, and fine-tuned by variable capacitor VC1 in the tank circuit. The coil L1 is wound in the form of a frame aerial to act as a search coil, the tuning

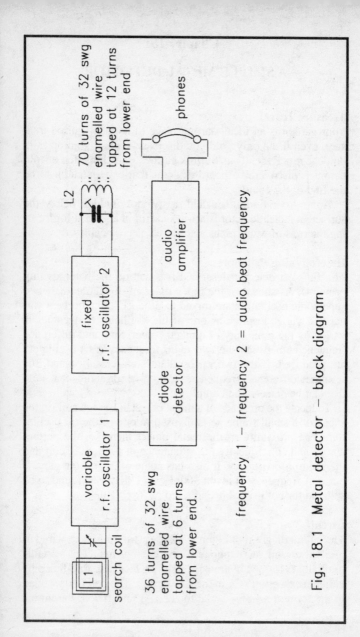

Fig. 18.1 Metal detector – block diagram

frequency 1 – frequency 2 = audio beat frequency

70 turns of 32 swg enamelled wire tapped at 12 turns from lower end

36 turns of 32 swg enamelled wire tapped at 6 turns from lower end.

phones

L2

L1

search coil

variable r.f. oscillator 1

fixed r.f. oscillator 2

diode detector

audio amplifier

126

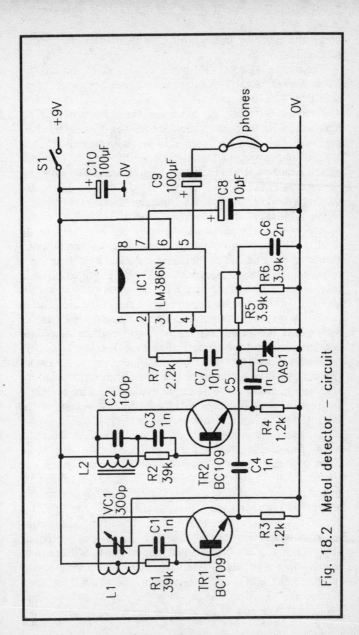

Fig. 18.2 Metal detector – circuit

being influenced by treasure trove, or more often, tin cans or rusty nails.

The fixed oscillator, TR2 has a similar circuit, but the coil L2 is wound on a quarter-inch former and fine-tuned by an adjustable iron-dust core.

If the two oscillators are tuned to differ in frequency by less than say, 3kHz, then this difference frequency is detected by diode D1. Since this frequency is in the audio range it is heard, after amplification, in the earphones. The output from the detector appears across the resistor load R5, R6. The capacitor C6 suppresses any high frequency signals that appear on the output of the detector. The audio output is routed via C7 and R7 to pin 2, the input of the audio amplifier IC1. The gain of this general-purpose amplifier (LM386) is set internally to 20 (26dB). This appears to be quite adequate for our purpose. However, the gain can be increased if desired by connecting a resistor and capacitor between pins 1 and 8. For example, a resistor of 1.2k in series with a 10μF capacitor will increase the gain to 50 (34dB); connect the negative end of the capacitor to pin 8. The output of the amplifier operates satisfactorily into an 8-ohm load, but for this application low to medium impedance earphones are probably preferable to a speaker.

Details of the two coils L1 and L2 are given in the circuit illustrations. If an oscilloscope or frequency meter is not available, an a.m. transistor radio can be used to check the oscillator frequencies. Switch the radio to the medium waveband, tuned to about 1MHz. Apply a short-circuit link across coil L1 on the metal detector and switch it on in the vicinity of the radio aerial. Tune through the medium waveband for the noise of the fixed oscillator signal. Check that this disappears when you switch off the metal detector. The iron dust core in coil L2 provides a means of fine tuning. If this frequency varies considerably from 1MHz, the value of capacitor C2 can be varied accordingly. With a satisfactory output from the fixed oscillator, remove the short-circuit link from the search coil L1 and apply it across coil L2. Check that the variable oscillator can be tuned within 1 or 2kHz of the frequency selected for the fixed oscillator on the MW radio. Remove the short-circuit link from L2 and the circuit should be ready for use. At switch-on, an audio beat note should be heard in the phones when VC1 is

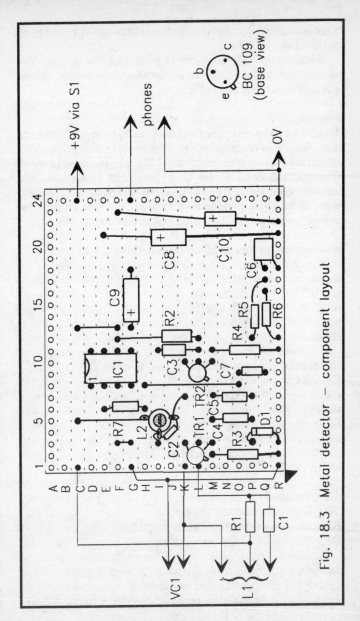

Fig. 18.3 Metal detector – component layout

129

tuned so that the variable oscillator is within one or two kHz of the fixed oscillator.

Tests showed that variations in pitch could be obtained for various metal objects, depending on size, over several inches with the search coil suggested.

Construction

The layout of the components (Figure 18.3) on the stripboard is not critical, but leads should be kept short to avoid unwanted interaction between the oscillators. The rear soldered connections are shown in Figure 18.4. Note that capacitor C2 is mounted on coil L2. There is scope for experiment, especially with the search coil (Figure 18.5) to get the best results. Try increasing the size of the search coil to improve its sensitivity.

Components for Simple Metal Detector (Fig. 18.2)

Resistors

R1, R2	39k (2 off)
R3, R4	1.2k (2 off)
R5, R6	3.9k (2 off)
R7	2.2k

Capacitors

C1, C3-C5	1nF (4 off)
C2	100pF
C6	2nF
C7	10nF
C8	10μF elect 10V
C9, C10	100μF elect 10V (2 off)
VC1	300pF variable

Semiconductors

TR1, TR2	BC109 (2 off)
IC1	LM386N audio amplifier
D1	OA91 signal diode

Inductors

L1	search coil (see text)
L2	iron dust-core coil on 6mm former (see text)

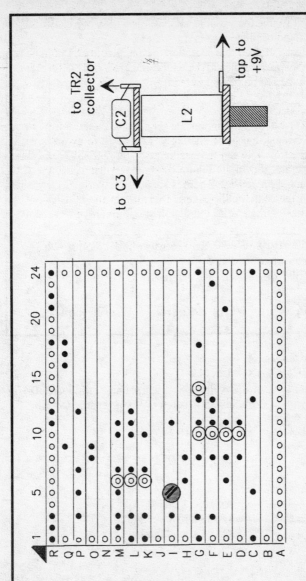

Fig. 18.4 Metal detector – copper strip layout and coil L2

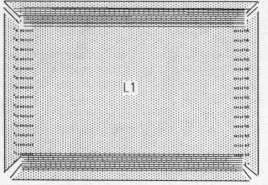

36 turns of 32 swg enamelled copper wire
wound on slotted Paxolin panel.
Coil tapped to +9V line at 6 turns from end.

Fig. 18.5   Metal detector — search coil

Miscellaneous
Project box, medium impedance earphones, stripboard, 0.1-in
(18 strips × 24 holes), 9V battery, 32swg enamelled wire for
coils, wiring, etc.

Chapter 19

ORNAMENTAL LIGHTING

Lighting Schemes

The use of lighting can transform your rock garden, pond or waterfall into a glittering kaleidoscope of colour, your flower garden into something magical, if it is done imaginatively. Many garden centres now stock in-pond lighting; floating and underwater lights and an interesting variety of lighting schemes with coloured discs set into fountain jets to produce rainbow effects.

Beside beautifying your garden by enhancing aquatic and floral displays, illumination has several practical uses after dark. It can lead you up the garden path, in the more helpful sense, indicate hazards such as steps, and generally improve security. In the interest of safety, only low-voltage lighting is discussed, but the general principles can be applied by qualified electricians who are capable of adapting the ideas to mains equipment.

Rather than adopting an overall lighting scheme, it is far better to contrast light and dark areas in a garden by highlighting certain features with a spotlight or two. Coloured lights are popular, but white or amber lighting appear to be 'top of the pops'.

Wiring Ways

If you know little or nothing about electrical wiring, or are a bit out of touch, here are a few more basic circuit details and guidelines that might help.

As we are limiting our projects to low-voltage supplies, if your lighting system is to be effective, think in terms of at least a 12-volt car battery to supply enough energy for a modest scheme. Always bear in mind that although the battery voltage is low it is not entirely harmless. A car battery, for instance, is capable of providing a lot of current in a circuit, especially if that circuit has low resistance. Good conductors of electricity such as copper, steel, iron, etc., have low resistance. Be careful that you don't connect the two terminals of a battery together with a piece of wire, or a screwdriver blade, otherwise a heavy current will flow, and your conductor will get decidedly over-heated. Insulate live battery terminals for safety and fit a suit-able circuit fuse as near to the battery as possible.

The current in a circuit can be limited by resistance. Although we can connect a resistance in a circuit to reduce the current to a safe value we must also remember that a circuit is intended to do something useful.

Low-Voltage Lamps

As power is the product of voltage and current it means that low-voltage lamps are rated at lower power than mains lamps. Generally, moderate power ratings are from about 10W to 36W, lower for the small MES bulbs. However, a brighter prospect than the usual tungsten filament lamp is the halogen lamp. This relative newcomer has become increasingly popular for window display lighting schemes. Halogen lamps are more expensive, but give about three times the illumination of tung-sten lamps for the same power rating. To get the most out of your low-voltage lighting, the advantages of halogen lamps are well worth considering.

Lamps in Parallel

If we take the simple circuit of Figure 19.1 we see that it contains a battery, two lamps and a switch. The current splits into two loops, which we call a parallel circuit. To get the most efficient use out of such a circuit, we must remember the rela-tionship between these electrical quantities, voltage, current and resistance.

From the few meter readings in the simple circuit the mean-ing of Ohm's Law becomes a little clearer. The potential dif-ference across the lamps is the voltage of the battery, 12V as seen if we apply a voltmeter across them. The total current, in the main loops, is $P/V = 4.4W/12V = 0.36A$. You can easily read this by connecting an ammeter in series with the battery. Note that the current in each parallel arm is $P/V = 2.2W/12V = 0.18A$, half the total current. (Nominal lumens per lamp = 11 – Maplin Buyer's Guide).

For a number of small lights, for example on a patio, we could extend this parallel arrangement: twenty 2.2W lamps in parallel take $P/V = 44W/12V = 3.6A$.

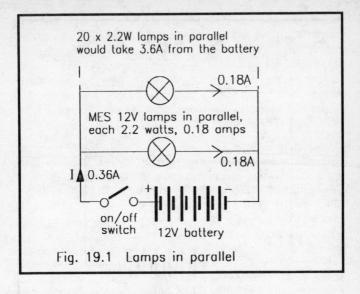

Fig. 19.1 Lamps in parallel

Lamps in Series-Parallel

The more current taken from the battery, the quicker it will become discharged. Eventually, its voltage will gradually drop from 12 volts and it will need charging. If you do not have a solar energy system then use a battery charger.

If you have a surfeit of lower voltage lamps you can use them with a battery in a series-parallel arrangement providing the total working voltage of the lamps in each series arm adds up to the battery voltage, and that they have the same current rating. Figure 19.2 shows such a circuit using two 6.5V lamps in series, in each parallel arm. Note that there is only half the battery voltage across each lamp, but the current through each lamp is 0.3A (nominal lumens per lamp = 12).

Two-Way Switch

Earlier in the chapter we looked at a simple light circuit and how to operate two or more lights from a circuit without over-loading the circuit or the lamps. It is also useful to know how to switch one light on and off from two different places. Two-

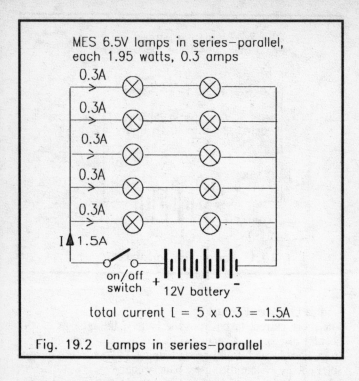

MES 6.5V lamps in series—parallel,
each 1.95 watts, 0.3 amps

0.3A

0.3A

0.3A

0.3A

0.3A

I↑1.5A

on/off
switch

+

12V battery

−

total current I = 5 x 0.3 = <u>1.5A</u>

Fig. 19.2 Lamps in series—parallel

switches are useful on stairways, in long alleys and also on garden paths as shown in Figure 19.3. Here, two lamps are shown in series, but this is quite incidental to the two-way switching; they are both 6V lamps so we need two in series if we are using a 12V supply. At switch-on, both lamps will light together and could be replaced by one 12V lamp.

The two-way switches at the house and greenhouse are changeover types. If you trace the wiring plan, you will see that the lights are shown switched on, because there is a complete series circuit from the positive terminal of the battery through the two switches and lamps back to the negative of the battery. If either of the switches is turned, the circuit will be broken and the lights will be off. Because we have a duplicate wire between the switches, if either switch is subsequently turned on the lights will come on.

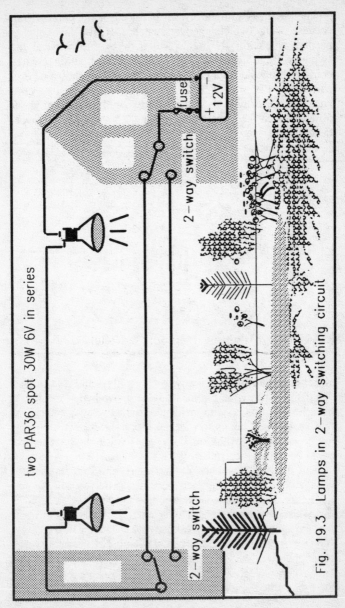

two PAR36 spot 30W 6V in series

fuse

+12V−

2-way switch

2-way switch

Fig. 19.3 Lamps in 2-way switching circuit

137

The circuit is straightforward but needs some extra wiring because of the two changeover switches. Heavy-duty cable is needed, single for the lights and a twin-cable between the switches. If the lights are fixed at ground level, all three wires could run together in a plastic tube. The circuit shown takes a current of: $P/V = 60W/12V = 5$ amps. A fuse must be connected in series with the battery and should be rated at about 50% overload; i.e. capable of carrying 7.5 amps without overheating.

Chapter 20

MOISTURE METER

A moisture meter can prove to be a life-saver in a garden. Appearances can be deceptive and plants that appear to be blooming in moist soil can be languishing around the roots. The surface indication can be deceiving, so we need to dig, or probe a little deeper to find out the true state of affairs. Why not build this electronic moisture meter with its sensing probe to make absolutely sure that your hydrangeas are not dehydrated?

The meter uses few components so can be easily made up as a small hand-held device. The heart of the circuit is the well-known LM3914 LED-display driver, a comparator IC that is capable of driving ten LEDs. The circuit uses its battery e.m.f. as a signal voltage derived via the soil resistance, and as an internal reference voltage for comparison. The wetter the soil, the lower its resistance, and consequently the higher the signal voltage.

Circuit

The circuit diagram, Figure 20.1, is wired in the bargraph mode to give a moisture reading, dependent on the signal input, by the output LEDs, D1 to D10. The reference voltage level at pin 8 can be set by the sensitivity control VR1 to vary the indication range of the display LEDs. A full-scale reading will cause all ten LEDs to light together. In very dry conditions the sensitivity control, VR1, may need advancing to encourage the lowest comparator circuit (pin 1), to light the left-hand LED (D1) on the bargraph display. A resistor of several hundred kilohms can be inserted in series with a probe wire if the moisture readings are too high.

Any supply voltage between 6V and 12V will be satisfactory. The device can take a current of up to 100mA at full-scale as each LED requires about 10mA, which is a little demanding for a small layer-type battery. However, if a hand-held unit is envisaged, then a PP3 battery gives economic operation if the LM3914 is wired in the dot mode. In this mode, only one LED is displayed at a time. This requires a slight

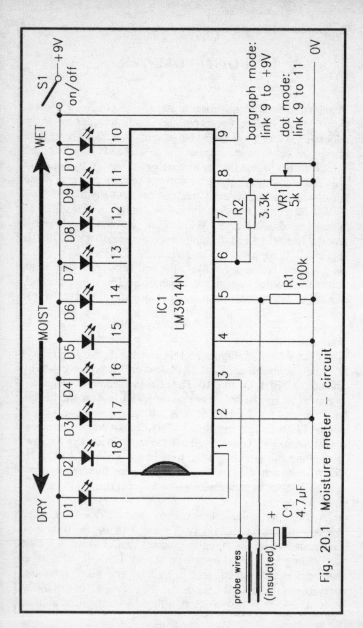

Fig. 20.1 Moisture meter – circuit

140

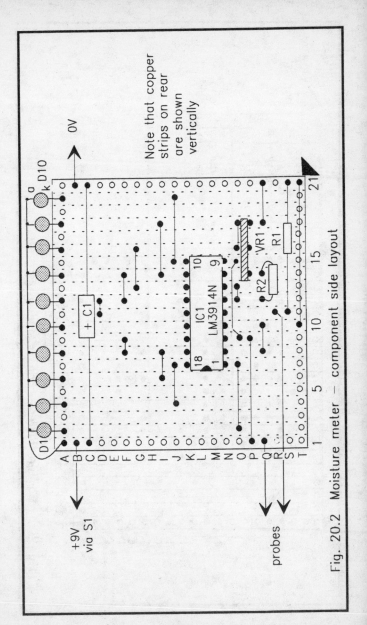

Fig. 20.2 Moisture meter — component side layout

141

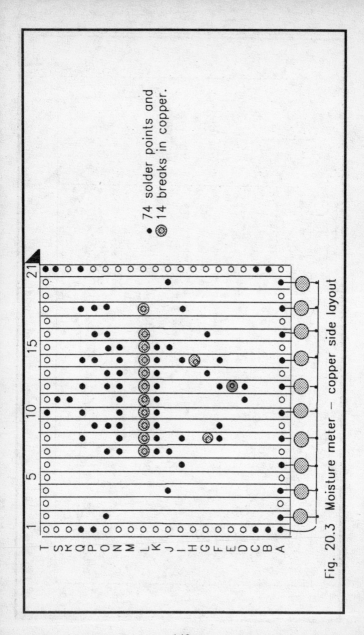

● 74 solder points and
◉ 14 breaks in copper.

Fig. 20.3 Moisture meter – copper side layout

142

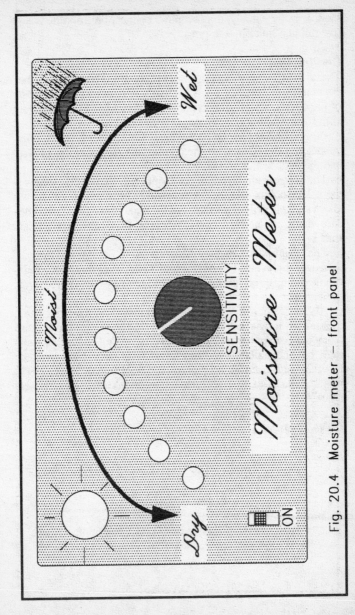

Fig. 20.4 Moisture meter — front panel

modification; namely, remove pin 9 connection from the positive rail and link pin 9 to pin 11.

Construction

The moisture meter is built on a stripboard layout around the popular 18-pin dual-in-line LM3914N integrated circuit. Most of the circuit has been incorporated in this LED display driver chip so few additional components are required.

Figure 20.2 shows the component side layout, the wire links connecting the IC pins to the appropriate tracks to the LEDs, and the battery and probes.

The copper side layout of the stripboard, Figure 20.3, shows the solder points and the breaks required in the copper strips. Use a suitable drill or special tool for making the breaks and be sure there are no whiskers of copper that can short-circuit tracks.

The front-panel display (Figure 20.4) could be further enhanced by using different colour LEDs, say three red, four orange and three green for a progressive dry–moist–wet indication.

Although control VR1 is shown mounted on the stripboard as a preset, it may be better to mount this on the front panel as a manual control to suit the various general soil conditions that may be encountered. In this case, take two leads twisted together, one from either side of the track break where VR1 was mounted, to two adjacent connections of a front panel control.

Components for Moisture Meter (Figure 20.1)

Resistors
R1   100k
R2   3.3k

Potentiometers
VR1   5k (preset or front-panel potentiometer as
            desired, see text)

Capacitor
C1   4.7µF elect 16V wkg.

Semiconductors
IC1   LM3914N display driver
D1 to D10   TIL209 LEDs (10 off, for colours see text)

Switches
S1   S.P.S.T. (on/off)

Miscellaneous
Plastic ABS project box, 0.1-in stripboard (21 strips × 20 holes), 9V battery (see text), wiring, etc.

Please note following is a list of other titles that are available in our range of Radio, Electronics and Computer books.

These should be available from all good Booksellers, Radio Component Dealers and Mail Order Companies.

However, should you experience difficulty in obtaining any title in your area, then please write directly to the Publisher enclosing payment to cover the cost of the book plus adequate postage.

If you would like a complete catalogue of our entire range of Radio, Electronics and Computer Books then please send a Stamped Addressed Envelope to:

BERNARD BABANI (publishing) LTD
THE GRAMPIANS
SHEPHERDS BUSH ROAD
LONDON W6 7NF
ENGLAND